Grasshoppers & Crickets

OF BERKSHIRE, BUCKINGHAMSHIRE & OXFORDSHIRE

JOHN PAUL

ILLUSTRATED BY CHARLOTTE MATTHEWS

Pisces
PUBLICATIONS

First published 1989 by Pisces Publications, Brasenose Farm, Eastern By-pass, Oxford.

British Library Cataloguing in Publication Data
Paul, John, 1959–
    Grasshoppers and crickets of Berkshire,
    Buckinghamshire & Oxfordshire.
    1. England. Crickets & grasshoppers
    I. Title
    595.7'26

ISBN 0-9508245-6-9

Typeset by DMD, Oxford
Printed by Bocardo Press, Didcot

405 411

595· 726

GRASSHOPPERS and CRICKETS of Berkshire, Buckinghamshire & Oxfordshire

CONTENTS

PREFACE

David Ragge's standard text on British grasshoppers and crickets is sadly out of print and the absence of a readily available text on these insects has resulted in their comparative neglect by entomologists and naturalists over the last decade. However, an excellent guide to British Orthoptera by Christopher Haes and Judith Marshall has just been published, so one can anticipate a resurgence of interest in these creatures. This book aims to provide the reader with some basic information on these insects as well as giving details of the regional fauna. The counties of the Upper Thames are richly endowed with Orthoptera, although they lack a number of British species that are limited in their distribution to the south coast. In addition to being of great interest in their own right, grasshoppers and their allies are important indicators of the quality and type of habitat and therefore a knowledge of this group is of benefit to the general naturalist.

ACKNOWLEDGEMENTS

Much gratitude is due to all who have submitted their records to the national and regional Orthoptera recording schemes. I thank Mr. E.C.M. Haes and Mr. J.M. Campbell for access to records held by the national and Oxfordshire recording schemes respectively. Dr. G.C. McGavin is to be thanked for granting my access to the Hope Entomological Collections, Oxford. Drs. D.R. Ragge and Judith Marshall and Mr. J. Reynolds of the British Museum (Natural History) have kindly read the type-script and made valuable comments. I am grateful to my publishers, Dr. D. Steel and Mr. P. Creed for their advice and to Charlotte Matthews for the fine illustrations.

'The Gracehoper was always jigging ajog, hoppy on akhant of his joyicity, . . .' *Finnegans Wake.* p.414.

John Paul, Oxford, April 1989

INTRODUCTION

Grasshoppers and crickets are really quite different insects: grasshoppers have short, relatively robust antennae, sing by rubbing their hind legs against their wings and are vegetarian; crickets have long thread-like antennae, sing by rubbing the bases of their wings together and are omnivorous. In Britain, at least, these generalisations hold true and provide a useful means of differentiating grasshoppers from crickets, although in other parts of the world there are exceptions to them, such as grasshoppers which have other mechanisms of sound production. Perhaps the most obvious features which grasshoppers and crickets have in common are the ability to stridulate (produce some sort of chirp or song) and long hind limbs which confer the power to jump. Grasshoppers are predominantly sun-loving insects whilst crickets and bush-crickets can be more active after dusk than during daylight hours. Although Britain's cool climate and isolation from the continent have not favoured the development of a profusion of species, many people would be surprised to learn that as many as ten distinct species of grasshopper breed on the British mainland, of which eight can be found in the region of the Upper Thames. Most of these can be identified by their song alone. There are also three species of groundhopper, four species of true cricket and ten species of bush-cricket breeding in southern England.

Locusts are particular species of grasshopper which tend to swarm and destroy significant amounts of vegetation including crops. A large number of species of grasshopper have been recorded as reaching plague proportions and have been called locusts. The two most important species are *Locusta migratoria* L. and *Schistocerca gregaria* (Forskal) and specimens from large swarms sometimes reach England. The British climate is not conducive to the development of destructively large swarms of grasshoppers. When not swarming, locusts exist in low numbers, causing little or no damage, like most other grasshoppers. Locusts cannot be identified by their size alone: there are many large species of grasshopper in the tropics and some locusts are quite small. Many cultures utilise locusts and other grasshoppers as a source of food and there are biblical references (e.g. Leviticus 11:22) to indicate the antiquity of such practices.

The general naturalist has much to gain from the study of Orthoptera (grasshoppers and their allies). They are delightful organisms. A working knowledge of the British species can be built up during one or two seasons as there are relatively few species in this country. Orthoptera make ideal subjects for close-up photography. Habitat assessment is greatly enhanced by including Orthoptera in such assessment as the British list includes species characteristic of all manners of terrain: limestone grassland, woods, heaths, bog and saltmarsh each have characteristic grasshopper faunas. Furthermore, the majority of species reach their peaks of abundance quite late in the year — from August to October — so it is possible to study Orthoptera at their best long after the seasonal decline of butterflies and other groups.

COCKROACHES

Cockroaches used to be classified with the grasshoppers and crickets as part of the order Orthoptera. They are clearly quite distinct in some ways and modern authors place the cockroaches (together with the mantises which do not occur in Britain) in their own order, Dictyoptera. Cockroaches are of ancient lineage, as attested by their abundant fossilised remains in certain coal measures. British cockroaches can be divided conveniently into two groups: native species which occur outdoors and introduced species which live in association with man and require an artificial source of heat. Only three species of cockroach occur naturally in the British Isles. All three are in the genus *Ectobius* and they are restricted in distribution to southern England and coastal areas of Wales. *Ectobius* species are small, elegant insects bearing little superficial likeness to *Blatta orientalis* L., the common pest species found indoors. The British *Ectobius* species inhabit heaths, chalk grassland, dunes and clearings in woods and are generally quite scarce except in a few favoured localities near the coast. None of them has been reported to be a pest in the British Isles. Nevertheless, when Linnaeus wrote the original description of one species found in Britain, *E. lapponicus*, he noted that it infested dried fish in the dwellings of the Lapps. Two *Ectobius* species can be found in Berkshire in wooded heathland: *E. lapponicus* and *E. pallidus*. The third British representative of the genus, *E. panzeri* is almost confined to sandy coastal localities, but there is a colony of it on sandy heathland in the inland county of Surrey and it might just occur in Berkshire.

The introduced species of cockroach can be subdivided into two groups: those that become established under artificial conditions in quasi-permanent colonies in this country and those that are imported sporadically on produce from overseas but cannot maintain colonies here. Those in the latter group comprise a long list of species but the reader is unlikely to encounter any of them unless involved in the inspection of imported goods and no further mention will be made of such species.

The Common Cockroach, *Blatta orientalis*, (also known as the 'black-beetle') is almost certainly our longest established pest species since it is mentioned by Thomas Moffet in his Theatrum Insectorum of 1634. This insect probably originated in Africa, but there are apparently wild, outdoor populations in the Crimea, so an Asiatic origin is possible. It requires the protection provided by man's buildings or rubbish dumps to prosper. This insect is especially associated with permanently heated institutions such as hospitals. It favours a temperature range of 20–28°C, lower than that of the other pest species in Britain. Other species found in heated buildings in Britain include the American Cockroach, *Periplaneta americana*, the Australian Cockroach, *Periplaneta australasiae*, the German Cockroach, *Blattella germanica* and the Banded Cockroach, *Supella longipalpa*. Despite their names, it is probable that all these species originated in Africa, where they still occur outdoors. All of them require higher temperatures than the Common Cockroach, e.g. 30°C for the American Cockroach. The Banded Cockroach seems to have become established in Britain as recently as a few decades ago, but is already present in many counties and will probably spread to many more. The Surinam Cockroach is a pest of botanical hot-houses, as it was at Thame Park, Oxfordshire at the start of this century. Both species of *Periplaneta* can infest hot-houses also and the author found dead examples of both of them on the paths in the hot-houses at Kew in October 1987.

Much has been written on the medical importance of cockroaches. It is doubtful that they are that important as vectors of disease, but it is a little disturbing from the public health point of view that cockroaches are quite mobile insects which feed readily on both human food and faeces and are known to be capable of harbouring and excreting a number of organisms known to be pathogenic to man, including *Salmonella, Streptococcus, Clostridium* and *Escherichia* species of bacteria and polio and hepatitis A viruses. Despite these facts there is little evidence in medical literature incriminating the cockroach as a vector of disease. Two notable instances where there is good circumstantial evidence of the cockroach as a passive vector are those of an outbreak of gastroenteritis due to *Salmonella typhimurium* on a paediatric ward in Belgium and of an outbreak of hepatitis A in California. In the first instance, cockroaches collected from the vicinity of patients at night were found to carry the culpable bacterium. Furthermore, cessation of the outbreak coincided with cockroach control measures.

Cockroaches can be a nuisance in places where they abound, such as parts of the tropics, since they wander over the sleeper at night and may feed on tears, the damp corners of the nose and mouth and on patches of skin. Afflicted persons may develop allergy to cockroaches. Cockroaches sometimes inflict bites by nibbling the sleeper and may become lodged in the nose or ears. Such problems must be very rare in the U.K. due to our comparative paucity of cockroaches. Some people detest the sight of cockroaches and some are frightened by them. Cockroaches tend to leave a characteristic and unpleasant smell. There are parts of the world where cockroaches are eaten by man as a food or medicine and earlier this century, extracts of these insects were employed by doctors in Europe as diuretics.

EARWIGS

Earwigs used to be included as a group within the order Orthoptera but now they have an order of their own, the Dermaptera. This is unfortunate because the Dermaptera as a whole have relatively few species worldwide and the group has consequently been ignored by many entomologists who favour the study of large assemblages of insects. Furthermore, many people detest earwigs, which are actually fascinating insects. In Britain there are five species of earwig known from outdoor situations. One of these, the spectacular and beautiful Tawny or Great Shore Earwig, *Labidura riparia* may be extinct. The Short-winged Earwig, *Apterygida media* is known only from counties on the east coast of England. That leaves three species which may be seen in the three counties. The Common Earwig, *Forficula auricularia* is extremely widespread in these islands and must occur in every ten km grid square in our area. It upsets gardeners by nibbling flowers and has distressed the author by eating Silver-washed Fritillary eggs by night in a butterfly breeding cage and by chewing through the bodies of butterflies on a setting board, leaving the wings intact. Earwigs probably eat quite a lot of garden pests. Many naturalists have observed the female Common Earwig tending her clutch of eggs which she keeps in a depression in the earth. The other earwigs found in the three counties are rather more scarce: Lesne's Earwig, *Forficula lesnei* and the Lesser Earwig, *Labia minor*. A number of other species are imported from abroad from time to time and may form temporary colonies.

CLASSIFICATION

Older authors placed such diverse groups as earwigs, cockroaches and grasshoppers in a single order and it is still convenient to discuss them in terms of their being Orthopteroids or Orthoptera in a broad sense.

Superorder ORTHOPTEROIDEA (Orthopteroids) (=Orthoptera *sensu lato*)

    Order DERMAPTERA (Earwigs)

    Order DICTYOPTERA (Cockroaches and mantids)
      Suborder BLATTODEA (Cockroaches)

    Order ORTHOPTERA *sensu stricto* (=SALTATORIA)
      Suborder ENSIFERA
        Superfamily TETTIGONIOIDEA
          Family Tettigoniidae (Bush-crickets)

        Superfamily GRYLLOIDEA
          Family Gryllidae (Crickets)
          Family Gryllotalpidae (Mole crickets)

      Suborder CAELIFERA
        Superfamily ACRIDOIDEA
          Family Acrididae (Grasshoppers)
          Family Tetrigidae (Groundhoppers)

One can talk about Orthoptera (Greek, meaning 'straight wings') in the general sense of the older authors as including the true Orthoptera — the grasshoppers and crickets (also known as the Saltatoria, or jumping forms) — as well as earwigs and cockroaches (the Cursoria, or running forms). All of these insects are fairly primitive in structure; hence their use as models of basic insect anatomy in schools. None of them has a complete metamorphosis as is seen in butterflies, beetles, ants, bees and wasps. That is to say that the Orthoptera lack a pupa or chrysalis stage as part of their transition from the egg to the adult insect. The young grasshopper, soon after it has hatched from the egg, looks superficially like the adult and simply becomes bigger with successive moults. On reaching the final moult, the insect acquires functional wings (unless it be one of the wingless or short-winged forms) and the apparatus for sexual reproduction, although it may be some days after the final moult before the insect is fully sexually mature.

ANATOMY

For the purposes of this book, the following labelled figures should suffice to illustrate the external anatomy of these insects.

Figure 1.
Lateral view of a locust, *Schistocerca gregaria*, to show external anatomy of a typical grasshopper.

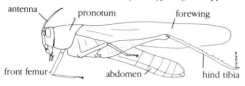

antenna / pronotum / forewing

front femur / abdomen / hind tibia

Figure 2.
Diagrams of the Meadow Grasshopper, to show length of forewings.

Figure 3.
Terminal segments of antennae of Rufous and Mottled Grasshoppers.

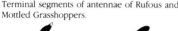

a. Rufous Grasshopper   b. Mottled Grasshopper

Figure 4.
Position of tympanum in Common Field Grasshopper

tympanum

Figure 5.
Shape of tympanum
a. Common Field Grasshopper
b. Heath Grasshopper *Chorthippus vagans*

a.   b.

Figure 6.
Dorsal views of pronota of six species of grasshopper to show their structure.
a. Lesser Marsh Grasshopper
b. Meadow Grasshopper
c. Common Field Grasshopper
d. Common Green Grasshopper
e. Woodland Grasshopper
f. Mottled Grasshopper

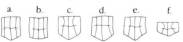

a.   b.   c.   d.   e.   f.

Figure 7.
Dorsal view of pronotum of Heath Grasshopper *Chorthippus vagans.*

Figure 8.
Pronota of Common Field Grasshopper to show range of variation in extent of dark markings.

Figure 9.
Forewings of grasshoppers.
a. Common Field Grasshopper 
Chorthippus bulge
b. Stripe-winged Grasshopper
large median area

Figure 10.
Forewing of Stripe-winged Grasshopper to explain terminology of pale markings.
stria postulnaris
linea scapularis
stigma

Figure 11.
Ovipositors.
a. Stripe-winged Grasshopper
b. Common Green Grasshopper

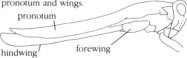

a.   b.

Figure 12.
Cepero's Groundhopper, *Tetrix ceperoi* to show pronotum and wings.
pronotum
hindwing   forewing

Figure 13.
Raised median keel of pronotum of Common Groundhopper

Figure 14.
Heads of groundhoppers.
a. Slender Groundhopper
b. Cepero's Groundhopper

Figure 15.
Lateral view of macropterous Roesel's Bush-cricket to show external anatomy.

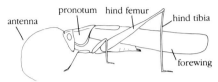

Figure 16.
Lateral view of pronota.
a. Roesel's Bush-cricket

b. Bog Bush-cricket

Figure 17.
Ovipositors of bush-crickets.

a. Oak Bush-cricket

b. Great Green Bush-cricket

c. Wart-biter *Decticus verrucivorus*

d. Dark Bush-cricket

e. Grey Bush-cricket *Platycleis albopunctata*

f. Bog Bush-cricket

g. Roesel's Bush-cricket

h. Long-winged Conehead *Conocephalus discolor*

i. Short-winged Conehead

j. Speckled Bush-cricket

Figure 18.
External anatomy of Common Cockroach ♂

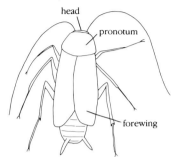

Figure 19.
Ootheca of German Cockroach

Figure 20.
Glandular hollow on seventh abdominal segment of *Ectobius* ssp
a. Dusky Cockroach *Ectobius lapponicus*
b. Tawny Cockroach *Ectobius pallidus*
c. Lesser Cockroach *Ectobius panzeri*

Figure 21.
Common Earwig ♂ showing external anatomy.

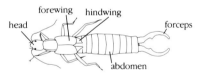

Figure 22.
Forceps.
a. Common Earwig ♂   b. ♀
c. Lesne's Earwig ♂
d. Lesser Earwig ♂
e. Short-winged Earwig *Apterygida media* ♂

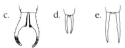

SCIENTIFIC NAMES

The beauty of binomial nomenclature, as originally applied to living organisms by Linnaeus in the eighteenth century, is that for each plant and animal we have a compact, unique, two word description which is of great help in the scientific study of these organisms. It allows communication between speakers of different languages. Each creature has a generic name, starting with a capital letter, which allocates the organism to a particular genus (e.g. *Chorthippus*) and a specific name, starting with a lower case letter, which identifies the species (e.g. *parallelus*). The two words together comprise the label which we use when talking about that species. Scientific names are usually derived from Latin or Greek and words of either language are used in a latinised form. Sometimes the names of people and places are used, appropriately latinised, as part of a scientific name. For example, there is *Tetrix ceperoi* Bolivar (a sort of groundhopper), described in honour of the Spaniard Cepero. Note that it is sometimes helpful to cite the author of the species (in this case Bolivar) after the scientific name, especially when it is first stated in the text. A scientific name should be underlined in writing, or printed in italics.

The reader who is unfamiliar with classical languages may find scientific names to be cumbersome, difficult to pronounce and hard to remember. In fact they are very useful and are essential for a serious study of these insects: below are stated the origins of the names of some of our Orthoptera to render them more meaningful and more memorable. A rough guide to pronunciation is given with each scientific name. The part of the word to be stressed is written in capital letters. Entomologists vary in how they pronounce scientific names. Some use anglicised pronunciations, using, for example, a soft 'c' (like a letter 's'), in '*Omocestus*' and a soft 'g' (like a letter 'j'), in '*albomarginatus*' and use ordinary English vowel sounds: others try to adhere to what modern scholars consider to be the probable pronunciations used by the ancient Greeks and Romans. Unfortunately, the academic pronunciation of Latin, as generally taught in schools, where for example, a letter 'c' is always pronounced hard and a letter 'v' like a 'w' is seldom used by biologists. One rule followed by many botanists and zoologists is to pronounce the letter 'c' softly after the letters 'i' and 'e'. A similar problem occurs with words of Greek origin: since they have been latinised for the purposes of scientific nomenclature it can be argued that their pronunciation should follow the same rules that one elects to apply to Latin words.

Furthermore, whilst many words of written ancient Greek are readily understood by the modern Greek speaker, it appears that pronunciation of many of the letters has changed greatly. In fact, as long as the stress is in the right part of the word, it should be understood readily by others, even when speaking with entomologists from abroad, whose pronunciation of scientific names is influenced by their own native language, just as our pronunciation of these names is usually partly anglicised.

Meconema thalassinum
MekoNEYma thalaSSEEnum

mecos, Gk. = length
nema, Gk. = thread
thalassa, Gk. = sea

Tettigonia viridissima
TettiGOnia viriDISSima

tettix, Gk. = cicada, grasshopper
tettigonion, Gk. = 'small, voiceless *tettix*'
viridissima, L. = most green

Pholidoptera griseoaptera
FoliDOptera grisayoAptera

pholis, Gk. = horny scale
griseus, L. = grey
a, Gk. = negative prefix
pteron, Gk. = wing

Metrioptera brachyptera
MetreeOptera braKIptera

metrios, Gk. = moderate
pteron, Gk. = wing
brachy, Gk. = short

M. roeselii rerZEllee

in honour of the entomologist Roesel

Conocephalus dorsalis
KonoCEfalus dorSAlis

conos, Gk. = cone
cephale, Gk.= head
dorsalis, L. = dorsal

Leptophyes punctatissima
LeptoFEYEees punctaTIssima

leptos, Gk. = delicate
phye, Gk. = stature
punctatissima, L. = most spotted

Tetrix subulata
TEtrix subooLAta

tetrix, Gk. = grouse
subulata, L. = awl-shaped

T. undulata undooLAta

undulata, L. = wavy

Stenobothrus lineatus SteynoBOthrus linayAtus	*stenos*, Gk. = narrow *bothros*, Gk. = hollow *lineatus*, L. = lined
Omocestus rufipes OmoCEstus ROOfeepayss	*omocestos*, Gk. = stitched together *rufipes*, L.= red foot
O. viridulus viriDOOlus	*viridulus*, L. = greenish
Myrmeleotettix maculatus MermeleoTEtix maculAtus	*myrmeleon*, Gk. = 'ant-lion' *tettix*, Gk. = grasshopper, cicada *maculatus*, L. = spotted
Gomphocerripus rufus GomfoCErippus ROOfus	*Gomphos*, Gk. = bolt *ceras*, Gk. = horn *hippos*, Gk. = horse *rufus*, L. = rufous
Chorthippus brunneus KORtippus BRUnayus	*Chort*, Gk. = pasture *hippos*, Gk. = horse *brunneus*, L. = brown
Ch. parallelus paraLElus	*parallelus*, L. = parallel
Ch. albomarginatus alboMARginatus	*albomarginatus*, L. = white-bordered

Note that the Greek root words have been transliterated here into Roman letters that best fit the spellings used in the scientific names.

VARIATION

Orthoptera exhibit numerous forms of variation. Some species are visibly more variable than others. Obvious features which vary include colour, pattern, size and wing-length. The greatest degree of variation seems to be found in a population that is expanding rapidly, as might be seen after exceptionally favourable weather. For example, in 1984 the hot, dry spring was ideal for the development of Orthoptera and macropterous forms (with abnormally long wings) were observed in numerous localities amongst populations of: Meadow Grasshopper,

Chorthippus parallelus; Roesel's Bush-cricket, *Metrioptera roeselii*; Long-winged Conehead, *Conocephalus discolor* (a species not found in our region). Similarly, in certain localities where the Meadow Grasshopper is always abundant, macropterous forms occur year after year. Such macropterism is thought to be a response of the growing nymphs to overcrowding and presumably aids the dispersal of adults.

Some species vary very little: British specimens of Oak Bush-cricket, *Meconema thalassinum*, Great Green Bush-cricket, *Tettigonia viridissima* and Speckled Bush-cricket, *Leptophyes punctatissima*, seem to have much the same size and colour regardless of their locality or season.

Many bush-crickets can occur as one of two distinct forms that are predominantly either green or brown. British species falling into this category include: Wartbiter, *Decticus verrucivorus*, (not known from our region), Bog Bush-cricket, *Metrioptera brachyptera*, Roesel's Bush-cricket, *M. roeselii*, Long-winged Conehead, *Conocephalus discolor*, and Short-winged Conehead, *C. dorsalis*.

Dark Bush-crickets, *Pholidoptera griseoaptera*, are always partly brown in colour, although certain localities seem to favour the occurrence of specimens with pale or reddish pronota. The Mole Cricket, *Gryllotalpa gryllotalpa* is always brown but museum specimens show variation in size.

The groundhoppers (Tetrigidae) are characterised by their greatly elongated pronota. In the Common Groundhopper, *Tetrix undulata*, in which the pronotum is relatively short, there is a very rare form in which the pronotum extends well beyond the tip of the abdomen. Conversely, in the Slender Groundhopper, *Tetrix subulata*, the typical form has a long pronotum; although in certain localities one often sees a form in which the pronotum (and wings) are much reduced, resulting in the insect's resembling typical *T. undulata*.

DISTRIBUTION

Climate seems to be a very important factor in limiting the distribution of Orthoptera. Most of the British species show strong preferences for places with high average values for temperature and sunshine. Many of the British Orthoptera not recorded from our region occur only in mild, sunny coastal localities. Local factors are important: south-facing slopes and woodland borders with a southerly aspect favour Orthoptera. Generally speaking, Orthoptera become increasingly scarce as one travels further north, until only a few cold-tolerant species remain (as is the case in northern Scotland). Even within our area it is noticeable that the Dark Bush-cricket, which is locally abundant in Berkshire, becomes a scarce insect in comparable habitat in north Oxfordshire (and it is a rarity in Warwickshire). None of the specialised boreo-alpine species, such as *Melanoplus frigidus* (Boheman), which is common in Lapland, is recorded from Britain. Rainfall does not appear to be an important factor in influencing the distribution of many species but it is noteworthy that the Lesser Marsh Grasshopper is especially common in the dry, eastern half of England.

The underlying geology of a locality accounts in part for its vegetation and hence its fauna. The Bog Bush-cricket is dependent on acid heathlands. The Rufous Grasshopper, *Gomphocerippus rufus*, is restricted to areas of calcareous grassland. All species show some degree of habitat preference.

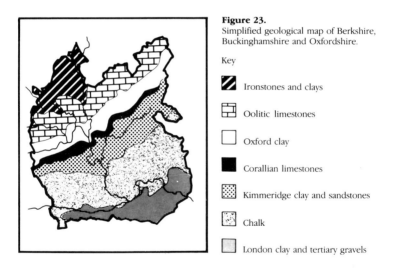

Figure 23.
Simplified geological map of Berkshire, Buckinghamshire and Oxfordshire.

Key

Ironstones and clays

Oolitic limestones

Oxford clay

Corallian limestones

Kimmeridge clay and sandstones

Chalk

London clay and tertiary gravels

Most of our British species are widespread in Europe and temperate Asia. The Slender Groundhopper occurs also in North America. Some species have a northern bias in Europe, such as the Common Green Grasshopper, which is common in Scandinavia but absent from the Mediterranean coast. Lesne's Earwig has an exceptional distribution amongst orthopteroids of the Upper Thames, being restricted abroad to France, Spain and Portugal: a pattern suggestive of the Lusitanian distribution patterns of some plants.

The species accounts which follow in the main text are accompanied by distribution maps. Where they are shown on a 10 km square basis, shaded squares on the periphery of the region may refer to records that pertain to neighbouring counties.

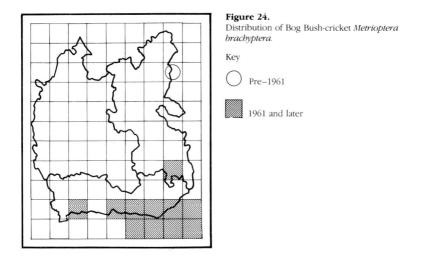

Figure 24.
Distribution of Bog Bush-cricket *Metrioptera brachyptera.*

Key

◯   Pre–1961

▨   1961 and later

SEASONAL APPEARANCE

Groundhoppers, unlike grasshoppers, overwinter as adults. They make their appearance in the first warm days of spring and are to be found in good numbers during April. Sometimes groundhoppers are roused to activity in mild spells during the winter months. Adults mate and lay their eggs in the spring months. The eggs soon hatch into nymphs which mature into adults by the autumn. The resulting adults hibernate and appear not to mate until the following spring. This simple scheme is followed quite rigidly by the Slender Groundhopper but is not strictly adhered to by the Common Groundhopper: some Common Ground-hoppers overwinter as nymphs and mature into adults during the summer. Thus it is possible to find populations of the Common Groundhopper composed of a mixture of the various stages.

Grasshoppers and bush-crickets overwinter as eggs which hatch during the spring. One sometimes sees the odd nymph as early as April but it is not until May or June that they become a prominent feature of their respective habitats. First instar nymphs can be very common in a locality where only a few adults remain later in the season. Some species mature faster than others: of the ones that occur in our region the Common Green Grasshopper and Mottled Grasshopper are noted for producing adults early in the season; often before the end of June. The greatest numbers of all our grasshoppers and bush-crickets occur in August and September, when much of the mating and egg-laying takes place. Some species, including the Oak Bush-cricket, the Dark Bush-cricket and the Rufous Grasshopper persist late in the season, surviving the early frosts to be seen in small numbers in November. It appears that many bush-cricket eggs pass two winters before hatching.

Earwigs are most evident as adults during late summer and early autumn. It seems as though all our species hibernate as adults. Generally only nymphs are to be found in late spring, but one can find occasional adult specimens of the Common Earwig at almost any time of the year.

THE THREE COUNTIES

The area of Britain that this book is concerned with consists of the three modern counties of Berkshire, Buckinghamshire and Oxfordshire. This is a region that is fairly representative of southern Britain as a whole, in terms of its orthopterous fauna. Here, the South of England blends with the South Midlands. There are no great conurbations within these counties, although Greater London lies immediately to the south-east. Their geography is dominated by the River Thames whose source is situated in Gloucestershire, not many miles west of the Oxfordshire border. From its source, the Thames flows eastwards to the ancient city of Oxford, then southwards to Goring, where the river divides the chalk hills of the Berkshire Downs and the Chilterns. Beyond the Goring Gap, the Thames flows on towards Reading, then along the southern edge of the Chiltern Hills until it reaches Surrey and Greater London. The Thames and its tributaries, such as the Evenlode, Windrush and Cherwell, are associated with marshes and damp meadows which provide important habitats for our wetland insects.

If one were to travel across this region from the northwest of Oxfordshire to the southeast of Buckinghamshire, one would cross a number of limestone scarps. Much of northern Oxfordshire consists of successive bands of Jurassic limestone, including oolite, forest marble and Stonesfield slate, but there is much overlying clay, much agriculture and little unimproved limestone grassland remains. Surviving fragments of such grassland include Westwell Gorse, a BBONT reserve near Burford; some downland on the north bank of the River Evenlode near

Stonesfield; and the green lanes (ancient, broad, unmetalled roads) near Spelsbury and Charlbury. None of these fragments appears to be especially rich in Orthoptera. In the far north of Oxfordshire, the underlying rock is ironstone, which imparts a lovely, rich tone to the stone-built villages in that region. On the ironstone hills along the Oxfordshire/Warwickshire border, one can find the Lesser Marsh Grasshopper in uncharacteristically well-drained, upland habitat. A narrow band of Corallian limestone crosses our region and is well represented near Oxford, where it gives rise to a fascinating patchwork of limestone grassland, woodland, calcareous fens and sandy heaths. The most impressive scarp of all is provided by the chalk of the Chilterns and Berkshire Downs. The chalk grassland is very rich in Orthoptera and other insects.

Along the southern fringe of Berkshire there is a lot of acid ground which supports some splendid remnants of heathland, such as occur at Greenham Common, Burghfield Common and Broadmoor Bottom. This part of Berkshire is also graced with much broadleaved woodland. A similar association of heath and old woodland is to be seen at Burnham Beeches in Buckinghamshire. The Chilterns are also well wooded. Famous woodlands in the north of the region include the excellent Bernwood Forest, Wytham Wood, Bagley Wood, Wychwood and Salcey Forest on the Buckinghamshire/Northamptonshire border.

COLLECTING

Collecting fulfills an important role in the study of these insects. There is only a small number of collections of British Orthoptera in existence, probably because the colours of most species fade after death making them unpopular subjects for display. The formation of private collections, provided they are properly labelled and preserved, would serve as a record for future entomologists. Specimens may be killed in the usual manner by placing them for fifteen minutes in a jar containing cotton-wool with a few drops of ethyl acetate. Alternatively, they may be kept alive and observed and their bodies preserved when they die off naturally. Taking specimens in late October (when Orthoptera are dying in the wild) would result in negligible effects on the future of the colony. Specimens should be pinned using entomological pins through the pronotum to the right of the midline. It is essential that the specimen bears a data label giving date and place of capture. When thoroughly dry, specimens may be arranged in cork-lined, air-tight storeboxes, containing vapona, naphthalene or paradichlorobenzene to deter pests. It is especially useful to collect specimens (e.g. a single male) from new localities where doubt may arise regarding identification. A reference collection thus formed is of great benefit to the entomologist. Detailed comparison of the different species facilitates one's ability to identify insects in the field. Collectors should ensure that scientifically valuable collections are eventually deposited in a suitable public museum. Special permission and good reasons are required in order to collect on such places as nature reserves. Rarer species should be collected with restraint (e.g. a single male at the end of the season). Some Orthoptera are protected by law (Wildlife and Countryside Act), including the Mole Cricket and two species not found in our region. Those readers who develop a real interest in Orthoptera will find collecting skills invaluable when they begin to investigate the wealth of fascinating but sometimes diagnostically difficult continental species.

BREEDING IN CAPTIVITY

It is an easy matter to keep Orthoptera alive in captivity in a suitable container by providing them with food and sunlight. Carnivorous species should not be kept with vegetarians and Great Green Bush-crickets should be kept singly lest they eat each other. Cockroaches will thrive amongst leaf-litter. Groundhoppers require moss, algae and damp sand for egglaying. Useful observations regarding their habits and genetics might be made. It is sometimes useful for purposes of identification to keep nymphs or recently moulted adults in captivity till they reach maturity.

Breeding from eggs laid in captivity tends to give disappointing results but by providing quasi-natural conditions, breeding could be accomplished. Given a miniature version of the insect's natural habitat in the lepidopterist's outdoor breeding tub, eggs might be overwintered and the early stages reared to adulthood.

PHOTOGRAPHY

Orthoptera are photogenic insects: their comparatively large size permits full-frame pictures using a minimum of special equipment; they are richly adorned with coloured patterns; with a little care they may be approached undisturbed. In addition to being a pleasurable pursuit for its own sake, insect photography has the advantage of producing a permanent record of the colour and posture of the living insect: Orthoptera preserved in collections tend to fade to a uniform brown colour. It is also useful to compile a photographic record of Orthoptera habitat. The author uses a 35 mm single lens reflex camera and 100 mm macro lens. Extension rings or bellows would be needed if the reader wished to photograph the groundhoppers, native cockroaches or smaller earwigs. Amongst films, Kodachrome 64 and Fuji 100 give good results. Strong sunlight often provides adequate lighting, but the reader may prefer to use flash. Photography of insects in their natural haunts often results in pleasing compositions. Orthoptera may be taken home in pursuit of technical excellence. Such specimens must not be released at unnatural sites.

GETTING TO KNOW THE SPECIES

By visiting the localities described below, in good weather at the right season, it should be possible for the reader to find the majority of Orthoptera native to the counties of the Upper Thames. One should take suitable outdoor clothing, including strong shoes, walking boots or wellingtons, depending on the nature of the site to be visited. A hand lens is useful for identification and may be hung around one's neck with a length of string. It is advisable to consult the relevant Ordnance Survey maps before visiting a locality. The 50,000 scale (or old one-inch) maps are adequate for most purposes. It might be difficult to locate some of the localities mentioned in the text below without reference to such maps. I have selected these localities because: they provide adequate public access; they are rich in Orthoptera; I happen to be familiar with these sites. There are numerous other good localities in our region which the reader might like to investigate for Orthoptera. Once familiar with the British species, the reader will be able to make significant contributions to our knowledge of British Orthoptera. Compared with popular groups, such as butterflies, our knowledge of their distribution is rudimentary.

ORTHOPTERA AT HOME

A number of Orthoptera may be observed in gardens, parks and on waste ground in towns. Others being characteristic inhabitants of hedges and roadsides may be found close to houses. Even in the centre of a great city some Orthoptera can be seen: in rural areas, of course, a greater variety of species is to be expected.

Of the grasshoppers, the Common Field Grasshopper, *Chorthippus brunneus*, shows a special affinity for manmade habitat. It is the grasshopper of roadsides, railway cuttings, quarries, urban carparks and the rough edges of parks and playing fields. In hot weather males fly several metres at a time and often enter gardens. The Meadow Grasshopper, *Chorthippus parallelus*, frequents lusher grassland than the previous species, but is to be found with it on many roadsides and fields close to human habitation.

The Oak Bush-cricket, *Meconema thalassinum*, inhabits a variety of trees, especially oaks and also the ivy on old walls. Because of its nocturnal habits and arboreal home, its presence in a garden may not be suspected until the chance discovery of a specimen made whilst harvesting fruit. In autumn, examples of the Oak Bush-cricket may be attracted to lights in houses. They are especially conspicuous on paths after having been dislodged from trees during high winds. Untidy gardens provide good habitat for the Speckled Bush-cricket, *Leptophyes punctatissima*. It favours rose bushes and shrubs. Specimens are sometimes brought into homes accidentally on rose cuttings. The Dark Bush-cricket, *Pholidoptera griseoaptera*, is a noisy insect whose chirps may be heard from July to November in nettle beds and road verges; especially in the south of our region. This species penetrates the suburbs of some towns on railway embankments. In those favoured places in the three counties where the Great Green Bush-cricket, *Tettigonia viridissima*, occurs, the naturalist may be lucky enough to have specimens of this spectacular insect singing in his garden. Such was the case at Cothill, Dry Sandford and Caversham in 1986.

The House Cricket, *Acheta domesticus*, used to be a common insect in the home. This is, alas, no longer so, although its monotonous chirp is still to be heard around the older hospitals.

BURGHFIELD COMMON: BERKSHIRE HEATHLAND

There are few surviving heathlands of any great extent in the three counties: Oxfordshire has virtually none; Buckinghamshire has some precious remnants at Stoke Common and Burnham Beeches; Berkshire has numerous patches of heath along its southern border. At Burghfield Common and neighbouring heaths and commons between Reading and the Hampshire border, one is able to find species that are very local in the three counties — the Bog Bush-cricket, *Metrioptera brachyptera*: the Woodland Grasshopper, *Omocestus rufipes*, and one of our native cockroaches, the Tawny Cockroach, *Ectobius pallidus*. A similar fauna is to be found a short distance away just over the Hampshire border at Silchester Common (Grid Reference: SU/623620); a locality well-known for its butterflies and wasps. Padworth Common (Grid Reference: SU/623646) is another site in the vicinity which has valuable open heathland. Although only small patches of heath remain at Burghfield Common, some are of high quality: one little triangle of heathland at the bifurcation of two roads (Grid Reference: SU/651663), supports the Bog Bush-cricket, the Tawny Cockroach and also the local Grayling butterfly. In warm weather at such a locality one might hear the chuffing song produced by the male Bog Bush-cricket. Despite the name, this insect inhabits quite dry heaths as well as bogs. It is almost always associated with some sort of heather where it may be photographed if approached with care. The Tawny Cockroach is an elusive and agile insect but one does find examples from time to time. Sometimes they sit exposed on bracken fronds but it is usually necessary to lift up branches of heather and search the ground for our native cockroaches. One must be cautious in so doing as adders tend to frequent such places. Another native cockroach with similar habits to *E. pallidus*, is the Dusky Cockroach, *E. lapponicus*: it has been recorded from Wasing and Aldermaston and could occur also at Burghfield Common.

The local Woodland Grasshopper may be sought in the Burghfield area. In 1983 it was abundant along rides in a conifer plantation between Ufton Nervet and Mortimer (Grid Reference: SU/636660). If one hears a grasshopper producing a loud continuous ticking song in such habitat it will be either the Woodland Grasshopper (which has white palps and a red abdomen) or the Common Green Grasshopper, *Omocestus viridulus*. The Woodland Grasshopper sometimes becomes locally abundant after the felling of woodland. It may be seen a few miles over the Hampshire border at Pamber Forest.

A number of more widespread Orthoptera occurs at Burghfield Common: Dark Bush-cricket, *Pholidoptera griseoaptera* and Speckled Bush-cricket, *Leptophyes punctatissima* under hedges and in brambles; Oak Bush-cricket, *Meconema thalassinum*, especially in oaks; Mottled Grasshopper, *Myrmeleotettix maculatus* on heathland; Common Field Grasshopper, *Chorthippus brunneus* and Meadow Grasshopper, *Chorthippus parallelus* in a wide variety of habitat; and actually on the ground itself, the Common Groundhopper, *Tetrix undulata*.

BERNWOOD FOREST

Bernwood Forest lies on the Buckinghamshire/Oxfordshire border to the east of Oxford. The Forestry Commission manages several blocks of woodland which comprise the forest. A substantial part of the forest, Waterperry Wood, lies in Oxfordshire; to the north in Buckinghamshire is a greater block of woodland, which includes Hell Coppice, Oakley Wood, York's Wood and Shabbington Wood. BBONT manages Whitecross Green Wood, an outlier of Bernwood on the edge of Ot Moor. Access is available to the public in all these woods along rides. The Forestry Commission provides a spacious carpark at the Horton-cum-Studley side of Oakley Wood (Grid Reference: SP/611117), the ride from which leads to the best Orthoptera site in the forest. Bernwood Forest is of national importance on account of its very rich, diverse assemblage of butterflies. It is a natural stopping point on the itinerary of the mobile entomologist. Compared with other sites north of the Thames, the Orthoptera are well represented: ten species may be found, including the local Woodland Grasshopper, *Omocestus rufipes*. Thus, Bernwood Forest is an excellent locality in which to learn to identify our Orthoptera. The best time to visit is on a hot day in August or September.

Along the hedges between the blocks of woodland, especially where there are untidy clumps of bramble, one should seek the Speckled Bush-cricket, *Leptophyes punctatissima*. They are well camouflaged but occasionally may be spotted basking on leaves in the afternoon. The Dark Bush-cricket, *Pholidoptera griseoaptera*, will be common in such habitat. It is abundant on many of the forest rides. Oak Bush-crickets, *Meconema thalassinum*, may be beaten from the branches of oaks. This species is actually more common on isolated oaks outside the blocks of woodland.

Walking eastwards from the carpark along the ride into Shabbington Wood one finds the Common Green Grasshopper, *Omocestus viridulus*. Males produce a loud continuous ticking noise. The colour varies from bright green to yellowish brown. This grasshopper frequents almost all of the grassy rides. Continuing eastwards one reaches a large open clearing where the ride crosses another ride running north-south. Where there is dry ground with sparse vegetation are colonies of the Common Field Grasshopper, *Chorthippus brunneus*. Males produce short chirps. They have long wings and fly for long distances when disturbed. The underside of the thorax is downy. Persistent searching may be required in order to find the rare Woodland Grasshopper. It prefers sunny patches of dry ground adjacent to conifers. The song is similar to that of the Common Green, but the palps are white and the underside of the thorax green. The abdomen is bright red in a mature individual. The Woodland Grasshopper reaches the northern limit of its known British range at

Bernwood Forest. In 1986 there were at least four small colonies in the forest, all of them being on sunny cross-rides. One colony was found in Waterperry Wood on recently cleared ground next to some conifers. There was one colony in York's Wood and two in Shabbington Wood within easy walking distance of the main carpark. Meadow Grasshoppers are generally common in the Bernwood clearings. Females have very short wings, exposing much of the abdomen. Both sexes have conspicuously brown knees.

The Lesser Marsh Grasshopper, *Chorthippus albomarginatus*, occurs in rather low numbers in a clearing close to the Hell Coppice pond. Therefore the novice is advised to seek this species in areas where it is easier to find. There is also a population of the Lesser Marsh in the clearings of Whitecross Green Wood. It is not a typical woodland insect.

On the ground, especially where there is a growth of moss and lichen, the Common Groundhopper, *Tetrix undulata*, is to be found. It is quite common in York's Wood and Waterperry Wood but is rather inconspicuous. Often the first sign of its presence is the clicking sound produced by an individual as it hops away, disturbed.

The Slender Groundhopper, *Tetrix subulata*, does occur in York's Wood, but is much easier to find in other localities such as Ot Moor and Whitecross Green Wood. At Whitecross Green Wood, the rides are being widened to encourage butterflies. In 1988 some of the resulting cut wood was burnt in piles along the edges of the rides to leave patches of scorched earth and ash. Such areas of blackened ground that remain after fires appear to be particularly conducive to the development of strong, temporary colonies of the Slender Groundhopper. Not only are the insects very easy to spot on the bare earth and ash, but also they do appear to flourish in large numbers.

WATLINGTON HILL: THE CHILTERNS

A variety of forms of downland turf, the presence also of densely vegetated slopes, together with some woodland makes Watlington Hill an ideal place to become acquainted with the Orthoptera of the Chilterns. August and September are good months in which to visit this locality. From a carpark at the top of the hill (Grid Reference: SU/708935) footpaths lead out onto the chalk downland. Close to the carpark there are shrubs and nettle patches where one might find two species of bush-cricket. The Dark Bush-cricket, *Pholidoptera griseoaptera* is common along roadsides on the Chilterns where there are sunny, sheltered verges with nettles and brambles. Both sexes may be found perched on vegetation in the sun. The strident, metallic chirps of the male may be heard late into the night. The Speckled Bush-cricket often occurs with the Dark Bush-cricket but its green coloration renders it rather inconspicuous. Its song is scarcely audible to man. A careful search of sheltered brambles on a sunny afternoon should reward the searcher. On the open downland of Watlington Hill one can see and hear five species of grasshopper, the easiest to identify being the diminutive Mottled Grasshopper, *Myrmeleotettix maculatus*. This grasshopper is the smallest in mainland Britain and has clubbed antennae. The best place to search for it is on the steep slope facing west towards Oxford. The Mottled Grasshopper seems to prefer well-drained habitat with patches of bare ground. Further down the slope one can find another local and distinctive species, the Stripe-winged Grasshopper, *Stenobothrus lineatus*. It shows a predilection for calcareous downland turf. The easiest way to learn to identify this insect is firstly to listen for the wheezy call of the male, which is unlike that of the other British Orthoptera. When one has heard this wavering, wheezy song it is time to seek the source: a glossy (usually green) grasshopper with red hind tibiae and a whitish mark on the forewings. The female is often to be found in the vicinity. On a hot day in August, the entomologist cannot fail to notice butterflies, including the Chalkhill Blue, *Lysandra coridon*, and the Silver-spotted Skipper, *Hesperia comma*, on this part of the hill. These butterflies often share sites with the Stripe-winged Grasshopper, showing a preference for the same sort of chalk turf. Three other more common species of grasshopper are to be seen on Watlington Hill. The song of the Common Green Grasshopper, *Omocestus viridulus*, is a loud continuous ticking noise, lasting about a minute. The colour is green or brown. The Common Field Grasshopper, *Chorthippus brunneus*, and Meadow Grasshopper, *Chorthippus parallelus*, are common on Watlington Hill, as they are on most semi-natural grassland in the three counties. The Meadow Grasshopper is easily identified by the wings' not extending beyond the hind knees; the hind knees are brown. The wings of the Common Field Grasshopper extend well beyond the hind knees. Females are large and are capable of flying several metres. The underside of the thorax of both sexes is downy.

Searches at ground level may reveal the Common Groundhopper, *Tetrix undulata*, although it is perhaps more profitable to look for this species, which hibernates as an adult, in April and May when the vegetation is less dense. At the far end of the hill, the footpath curves round the slope descending through woodland, where the arboreal, pale green Oak Bush-cricket, *Meconema thalassinum* occurs; individuals may be beaten from trees or dense clematis onto a sheet or upturned umbrella.

Thus on the right day one might find nine species of Orthoptera on Watlington Hill: a good total which includes two local species, the Mottled and Stripe-winged Grasshoppers. These notes could be applied to other areas of the Chilterns and Berkshire Downs, wherever good south-facing turf remains. Visitors to the slopes between Goring and Reading may find a grasshopper unknown at Watlington, the Rufous Grasshopper, *Gomphocerippus rufus*: it bears clubbed antennae with white tips. Hillsides which are partly overgrown with shrubs sometimes harbour the spectacular Great Green Bush-cricket, *Tettigonia viridissima*. It is unrecorded at Watlington but can be seen on two BBONT reserves in the Chilterns: Warren Bank (access limited to members) and Buttler's Hangings.

THE BERKSHIRE DOWNS

At Goring, the Thames divides the chalk of the Chiltern Hills from that of the Berkshire Downs. Despite their geological similarity, the two areas differ markedly in character: the Berkshire Downs are relatively open treeless, arable lands; the Chilterns are subject to less intense patterns of agriculture, having substantial blocks of woodland and much permanent pasture. The contrast can easily be demonstrated by comparing the views obtained on journeys by car across the Berkshire Downs from Newbury towards Abingdon on the A34 and the busy route over the Chiltern Hills on the M40 motorway. The two areas have comparable orthopterous faunas but that of the Chilterns is richer with recent records for Rufous and Woodland Grasshoppers and for the Great Green Bush-cricket, whilst there appears to be no recent report of these insects from the Berkshire Downs. Since the reorganisation of local government in 1974, much of the Berkshire Downs has been transferred to the county of Oxfordshire, including entomologically important downland around the White Horse above Uffington.

A locality rich in Orthoptera, which remains in Berkshire, is Lough Down, a National Trust property above Streatley at the eastern end of the Berkshire Downs. Like Watlington Hill, Lough Down is a good place to become acquainted with the local Stripe-winged Grasshopper, *S. lineatus*. The locality has the advantages of adequate parking space and public access. The best time to visit would be on a hot sunny day in August or September. The car park (Grid Reference: SU/583807) is at the top of a steep narrow lane which rises from a set of traffic lights in Streatley. One might also enter the down at its lower end by foot from Streatley. Lough Down is the home of four species of grasshopper. As one walks from the car park, one comes to a gently sloping area of coarse grassland. Two species of grasshopper commonly occur here: Common Green Grasshopper, *O. viridulus* and Meadow Grasshopper, *C. parallelus*. The Common Green is easily distinguished by its prolonged, ticking call; the Meadow by its shortened wings. Beyond the coarse grassland, there is a large patch of scrub where common species of bush-cricket might be sought. The main path leads over the top of the down, avoiding the scrub until a steeply sloping area of well-grazed downland is reached which faces Streatley and the Goring Gap. This short downland turf is a good place to find the Stripe-winged Grasshopper. The wheezy calling song of the male is unmistakable, but the courtship song is different, being a ticking noise that sounds like a very quiet Common Green Grasshopper.

The Common Field Grasshopper abounds on this slope. In many of its localities, this insect occurs only as a mixture of dull grey and brown forms. In a few places, such as Lough Down, there is a spectrum of bright colour variations. Brown and grey varieties (striped, mottled or plain) predominate but reddish, buff and partly green forms also occur. Specimens which are green above with brown sides are not rare, but in September 1986, the author had the good fortune to find a female that was entirely green apart from the wings which were brown. Dr. D.R. Ragge calls this form 'var. green' and it is seldom recorded. Whatever colour they are, Common Field Grasshoppers are easily distinguished by their comparatively large size, shape of pronotum, bulge in margin of forewing and downy underside of thorax.

COTHILL: ON CORALLIAN SANDS

Running in a band from Dorset to Yorkshire, the Corallian deposits are well exposed in our region along a strip of ground extending from near Faringdon in the West to the Oxford district in the East. The Corallian strata represent the remains of prehistoric coral reefs and ancient sands. This varied geology generates a diversity of habitats, rich in natural history. Near the village of Cothill, a few miles west of Oxford, there is an especially good collection of sites, all within walking distance of the village. Types of habitat include woodland, limestone grassland, old sand-pits and calcareous fens. At least ten species of Orthoptera occur in this small area. Furthermore, it is notable that the local Lesne's Earwig, *Forficula lesnei*, is common in one locality. The hedges and fields around

Cothill contain good numbers of the spectacular Great Green Bush-cricket, *Tettigonia viridissima*, a species known from few inland localities in Britain.

A good place to start looking for Orthoptera is at BBONT's excellent Dry Sandford Pit Nature Reserve (carpark: grid reference: SU/467995). Much of the reserve is open to non-members. In warm weather, the Great Green Bush-cricket begins singing about the middle of the afternoon and continues singing late into the night. The season for adults in Oxfordshire stretches from late July till mid-October, reaching a peak of activity around the end of August. The song consists of long bursts of strident metallic stridulation. With good hearing it may be detected at a distance of two hundred yards. Older persons may find the song less obvious, the high-pitched components of the song being outside their range of hearing. With the car window wound down on a hot evening in August or September one can drive round the lanes between Tubney and Boars Hill and count male Great Greens stridulating in roadside hedges and gardens. The Dry Sandford Pit Nature Reserve contains a strong population of this lovely insect. It is to be sought on brambles and shrubs. It takes practice to approach and actually see a stridulating male, even though it is bright green and several inches long. Females are often present near the males. Sometimes males can be spotted sitting on twigs at the top of trees. There are plenty of old specimens of the Great Green, which originated from the Cothill district, in the Hope Collections in Oxford, indicating that the present population is an established feature of the area. As an alternative to searching for adult Great Greens, one could try seeking the nymphs in May or June. There must be quite a high mortality amongst the developing nymphs as they are quite easy to find at a locality where only a scattered population of adults is to be found later in the season. The first instar Great Green is about a quarter of an inch in length and is pale green in colour. There is a pale brown, dorsal stripe. In a warm season, nymphs can be found from early May onwards. In an average season, mid-May is a good time to search: there should be plenty of nymphs about and also the sparse vegetation so early in the season renders them easier to find. On 12 May 1988 at Dry Sandford Pit, the author saw a first instar Great Green on a buttercup. During the same visit an adult Slender Groundhopper, *Tetrix subulata*, was found amongst algae by one of the pools.

The colour of the Oak Bush-cricket is much the same as that of the Great Green, but the former is much smaller. It may be beaten from oaks and other trees around Cothill; it is common in the Dry Sandford Pit. The

Dark Bush-cricket is common also throughout the Cothill district. Two species of grasshopper, the Meadow and Common Field, are abundant in the Dry Sandford Pit.

The Dry Sandford Pit is graced by the presence of a rare earwig: Lesne's Earwig, *Forficula lesnei*. It is common on oaks bordering areas of long grass and the best season for it is September. The Common Earwig, *F. auricularia*, occurs with it, but the two species are very distinct, *F. lesnei* being smaller with paler legs and distinctive forceps (see key and main text). Lesne's Earwig is present at another Corallian site, Sydling's Copse Reserve, east of Oxford. Sydling's Copse is adjacent to Wick Copse (which is the only name given of the two sites on the 50,000 scale ordnance survey map) and is probably synonymous with a locality called Headington Wick in the older literature. Walker found Lesne's Earwig there in November 1906 and this beautiful insect was still present when the author visited the locality in October 1986.

Cothill is famous amongst botanical circles for the calcareous fenland to the north of the village. Here grow marsh orchids, butterwort and cotton grass and this is where Prof. E.B. Ford studied the genetics of the Scarlet Tiger Moth. Part of the fenland — Parsonage Moor — is a BBONT reserve and cannot be visited without written permission. Parsonage Moor has few species of Orthoptera, but it is worth noting the presence of an isolated colony of the Common Green Grasshopper, *Omocestus viridulus* on the northern part of the reserve. A small National Nature Reserve, known as the Ruskin Reserve, is situated further along the fen. The Slender Groundhopper, *Tetrix subulata*, lives by the pond; in 1987, numerous individuals were seen to have colonised deposits of ash left after the burning of cleared scrub.

To the west of Cothill and north of the minor road is an expanse of dry sandy terrain. By walking along public footpaths near Hitchcopse Farm, one passes more prime habitat for the Great Green. In 1986, the Great Green was common around Hitchcopse Farm in hedges, cornfields and waste ground. Much of the area is devoted to the commercial extraction of sand deposits and the Great Green thrives in the scrubby vegetation in neglected sand pits. One pit is maintained as a BBONT reserve (Hitchcopse Pit, grid reference: SU/452996) and is distinguished by the presence of the Mottled Grasshopper, *Myrmeleotettix maculatus*. The Mottled is quite a scarce insect in the three counties and seems to require well-drained rocky or sandy soils. Another site for this insect on the Corallian exposures is a small rabbit-grazed clearing in Wytham Wood, a few miles north of Cothill.

Further west are the remnant heathlands of Frilford Heath near Tubney. The heath was turned into a golf course before the last war, but still has patches of heather. Access is restricted but it is worth visiting the area just to view the heather from the roadside. Much of the Hope Collections' series of Mottled Grasshopper was derived from this site in the early part of this century. Also in the Hope Collections is an old specimen of the Short-winged Conehead from Tubney: there is no recent Oxfordshire record for this species. The village of Besselsleigh, just north of Tubney was once the home of the Mole Cricket.

BINSEY: THE THAMES OR ISIS

The Lesser Marsh Grasshopper, *Chorthippus albomarginatus*, is probably under-recorded in our region. There are recent records from Ot Moor, Hell Coppice and meadows bordering the Thames and Evenlode; also dry, furzy grassland on the Warwickshire/Oxfordshire border. Once seen and heard this is an easy species to identify, but it is useful to 'get one's eye in' at a known locality.

Binsey is just outside Oxford on the west side of the river, opposite the famous Port Meadow. Binsey can be reached via Binsey Lane off the Botley Road west of Oxford railway station. From the footpath along the river bank near the Perch public house a number of fields can be seen which contain a population of the Lesser Marsh Grasshopper. This sought after species congregates in sheltered spots by the footpath in hot weather. In such congregations, the courtship songs of the males produce a chorus. The Common Field and Meadow Grasshoppers also occur at Binsey.

ORTHOPTERA AT NIGHT

Some Orthoptera and many Dermaptera are more active after dusk than they are during the day and are hence easier to find at night. Moth collectors and other naturalists may already be aware of this phenomenon. Of the bush-crickets, the Dark Bush-cricket, *Pholidoptera griseoaptera* and the Great Green Bush-cricket, *Tettigonia viridissima* may be heard singing at almost any time of day in warm weather but are especially sonorous during the evening. At night one is able to illuminate these insects by torch-light to observe them very closely. By contrast, they are usually very wary of the observer during the day. Under cover of darkness, Oak Bush-crickets, *Meconema thalassinum*, prowl around the branches of trees and may be seen crawling around on shrubs. The females creep onto tree trunks to oviposit. The introduced House Cricket, *Acheta domesticus*, becomes active after dark. In hot weather they may leave the protection of buildings to wander over paths and fields. The Mole Cricket, thought to be extinct in our region is nocturnal. By day our earwigs tend to remain hidden under stones and amongst vegetation. At night they may be observed by torch-light foraging.

The grasshoppers, groundhoppers and remaining species of bush-cricket are usually diurnal but during unusually hot weather many of them can be heard singing late at night. The Slender Groundhopper, *Tetrix subulata*, (which is mute) has been reported as occurring at the lepidopterist's illuminated sheet at night.

ORTHOPTERA ABROAD

The reader who travels beyond the three counties in search of Orthoptera will become aware of striking differences between Orthoptera faunas, in terms of their abundance and diversity, in the various regions. Coastal areas are generally richer than inland areas and northern localities tend to have fewer species than the comparatively warm and sunny south. Several species of British Orthoptera are restricted to localities near the south coasts of England and Wales: the Scaly Cricket, *Pseudomogoplistes squamiger*, is confined to Chesil Beach, Dorset; the Field Cricket, *Gryllus campestris*, is now known only from West Sussex; Heath Grasshopper, *Chorthippus vagans* is restricted to Hampshire and Dorset heaths; Cepero's Groundhopper, *Tetrix ceperoi* Bolivar is confined to localities near southern coasts; the Grey Bush-cricket, *Platycleis albopunctata* is seldom found more than a few hundred yards from the sea; the Wartbiter, *Decticus verrucivorus* is confined to a few sites in southern counties. Other species are more widespread but with a clearly southern bias: the Wood Cricket, *Nemobius sylvestris* is known from only six southern counties but can be abundant in the New Forest; the Long-winged Conehead, *Conocephalus discolor* was a great rarity of the south coast a few decades ago, but is now spreading inland. None of these insects is recorded from the three counties, but we do have all the other Orthoptera known in mainland Britain.

The east coast of England is a little colder than the south coast and has correspondingly fewer species. Two species of Orthoptera, however, come into their own in the east of England. Roesel's Bush-cricket is abundant over wide areas of saltmarsh and rough ground in Essex and Kent and in the region around the Wash the Lesser Marsh is the most common species of grasshopper. The various ranges of chalk and limestone hills in southern England have similar orthopterous faunas to those of the Chilterns and Berkshire Downs, but each area has its own subtle differences. For example, the North Downs of Surrey and the South Downs west of the Arun are particularly rich in sites for the Rufous Grasshopper. The low Liassic hills of Somerset provide another focus of richness for the Rufous Grasshopper, but in Somerset, our other downland grasshopper, the Stripe-winged is curiously scarce. In the southwest of England and in Pembrokeshire, the Great Green Bush-cricket is a conspicuously common insect, colonies occurring at close intervals all the way from Land's End to the Isle of Purbeck on the south coast and from Cornwall to Portishead along the Bristol Channel.

Of the lowland heath areas of Britain, the Isle of Purbeck and the New Forest have especially good localities for Orthoptera. Here one might find the Large Marsh Grasshopper and the Bog Bush-cricket. The Bog Bush-cricket is also well represented on the bogs and heaths of the western part of the Weald. Away from these areas, its distribution becomes more scattered. In the English Midlands north of Oxford, Orthoptera become distinctly thin on the ground. Here the Bog Bush-cricket is a rare insect restricted to just a few choice localities. It is curious also how the Dark Bush-cricket, which fills the night air of southern England with so much sound, becomes so scarce, occurring in a few south-facing woods and warm valleys.

In upland Britain, on the moors of Wales, northern England and Scotland there are very few species of Orthoptera, a typical site having only two species of grasshopper, the Meadow and Common Green, perhaps with Mottled grasshopper on dryer portions of heathland; but there will be no bush-crickets, except perhaps for the Bog Bush-cricket in low-lying areas. Nevertheless, it is quite as thrilling to find two or three species of grasshopper when the sun shines on a Hebridean island as it is to see fifteen or more species of Orthoptera in a day on the Isle of Purbeck.

Those who wish to see all the British Orthoptera may make a pilgrimage to Langness on the Isle of Man for the Lesser Mottled Grasshopper. This smallest of British grasshoppers is known from nowhere else in the British Isles. In mainland Europe there are hundreds of species of Orthoptera not found in Britain. As close to England as Calais one can see *Chorthippus biguttulus*, there the most common species of grasshopper: it is very like our Common Field Grasshopper but with a totally different metallic song.

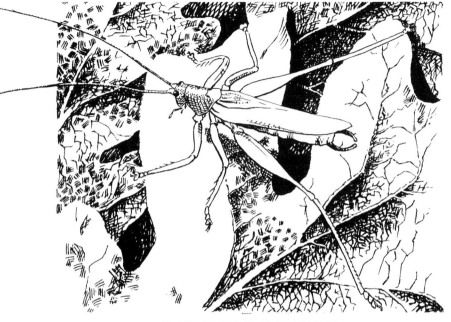

OAK BUSH-CRICKET
Meconema thalassinum (Degeer)

Oak Bush-crickets are about 15 mm long, fully-winged and of a delicate pale green colour. The male bears large pincer-like appendages at the end of the abdomen. The ovipositor is gently curved. They do not stridulate as such, but males drum leaves with their hind legs. Oak Bush-crickets seldom mature before August and may persist until December.

M. thalassinum lives in trees, including pear, sallow, ash, field maple and especially oaks. They are nocturnal, but during the day can be beaten from the branches of trees and thus are often noticed by lepidopterists who are beating for larvae. Beating is one of the most effective methods of acquiring specimens of this insect and of detecting its presence in a new locality. At night, these bush-crickets may be observed by torch-light crawling amongst foliage; the females may be seen ovipositing in the crevices on tree trunks. After autumnal storms, when these insects have been dislodged from their trees (or should they leave their trees voluntarily), they may be seen on paths or roads and may be attracted to lights in people's homes. Occasional specimens are seen on roads, paths and fences and on cars that are parked under trees: in such places they are most conspicuous. It is sometimes worthwhile to examine cobwebs for dead examples of this species, especially webs that are formed under the eaves of buildings close to woodland. Because this insect is attracted to light, other places to look for its remains are the spiders' webs around windows and the window sills themselves.

The Oak Bush-cricket is widespread and might be anticipated to occur in every 10 km square in the three counties. It is common in the Oxford district, where localities include: Headington, Shotover Hill, Brasenose Wood, Southfield Park, Kidlington, Prattle Wood, Elsfield, Waterperry Wood, Whitecross Green Wood, Beckley, Beckley Common, Horton-cum-Studley, Cothill and Chilswell Hill. It is common in the Chilterns, where localities include: Watlington Hill, Bix Bottom and Turville Hill.

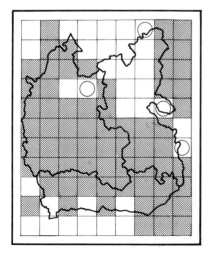
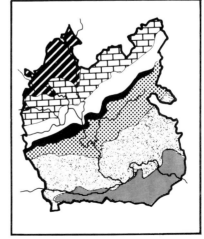

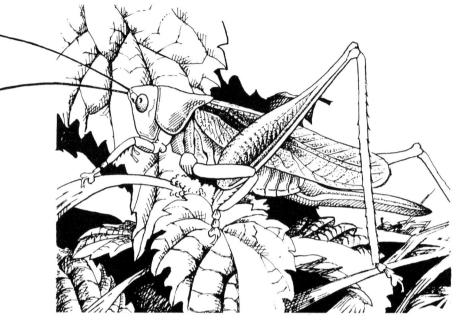

GREAT GREEN BUSH-CRICKET
Tettigonia viridissima (L.)

Being over 4cm in length and bright green in colour, this insect is easy to identify. Some authors call it the Great Green Grasshopper but its long, thread-like antennae and other features show that it is really a species of bush-cricket. The wings are well developed and enable the insect to fly. The song is metallic in nature and very loud: with good ears one can hear it at a distance of several hundred yards. Each burst of song may last several minutes. The majority of males begin to sing during the afternoon and continue to sing late into the night. The song may be heard from late July till mid October.

Despite its large size and loud song, *T. viridissima* may be a rather difficult insect to find, as the males cease stridulating if disturbed. If one wishes to visualise the insect one should approach very carefully. Males often perch high up on trees and bushes; also on lower plants such as thistles and even on wheat in the middle of corn fields. If handled they may exert a painful but harmless bite. They will attack and devour other insects, including individuals of the same species if placed in the same container. Untidy hedges provide the best habitat and they often stray into gardens.

Oxford is near the northern limit of this insect's range in Britain. The best area for it in our region seems to be the Corallian ridge between Faringdon and Oxford, from which area there are numerous historic specimens in the Hope Collections, Oxford, bearing data for such localities as Marcham and Tubney. It was numerous around Cothill in 1986 and 1988. It seems to have died out in its old haunts east of the Thames at Oxford. There are old specimens in the Hope Collections from: 'The Parks'; Lye Hill; Noke; and 'near Woodeaton'. The Chilterns support at least two colonies; one in Oxfordshire at Warren Bank and one in Buckinghamshire at Buttler's Hangings. There were good numbers of first instar nymphs amongst the coarse turf at Warren Bank on 21 May 1988. There are recent reports from Caversham and Wraysbury in Berkshire. This species occurs on at least four BBONT reserves.

In the mid-1980s, a female of this species was captured on a wall in Hayfield Road, Oxford and was reliably identified before being released into a garden in that area. This find raises a number of possibilities, the most exciting being that there is a chance that a colony of this insect persists on rough ground in north Oxford. Lucas (1920) lists Binsey as a locality for this insect, although the author has failed to locate it at that site. Hayfield Road is close to the semi-natural Port Meadow and the Trap Grounds. Other possibilities are that the insect had been deliberately released or that it had flown there from the Cothill district in warm weather.

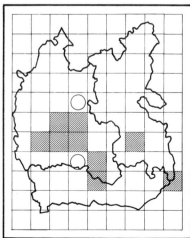
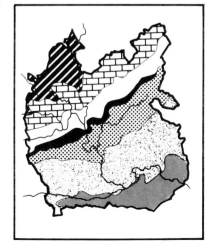

DARK BUSH-CRICKET
Pholidoptera griseoaptera (Degeer)

The male is dark brown with pale, vestigial wing-flaps. The female is fawn in colour with hardly any trace of wings. The total length of males and females is about 15 mm. The underside of the abdomen of both sexes is pale yellow-green. They are bulky insects. The song consists of short strident chirps. In spring the small, dark, agile nymphs may be quite conspicuous on low vegetation. Adults are heard from late July till October (November in a mild autumn). This species is often common in sheltered localities quite late in the season, when other Orthoptera have died off. In many seasons one is able to witness vigorous noisy colonies of this insect on mild days in late October. Sometimes males can be heard stridulating in November, even after the onset of autumn frosts.

Typical habitat consists of nettles and brambles under hedges, in large, untidy gardens, or along woodland rides. In Berkshire and the Chilterns it seems to be ubiquitous in such habitat. Around Oxford it is locally common, localities including: Bernwood Forest, Whitecross Green Wood, Brasenose Wood, Headington Quarry, Bullingdon Bog, Wychwood Forest, Holly Wood, Stanton Great Wood, Ot Moor, Beckley Common,

Prattle Wood and Tubney. In north Oxfordshire it is a scarce insect. It is common in Salcey Forest on the Buckinghamshire/Northamptonshire border.

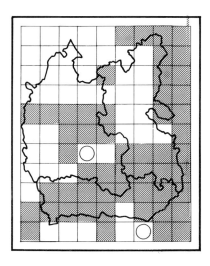
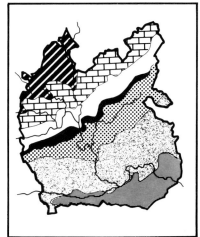

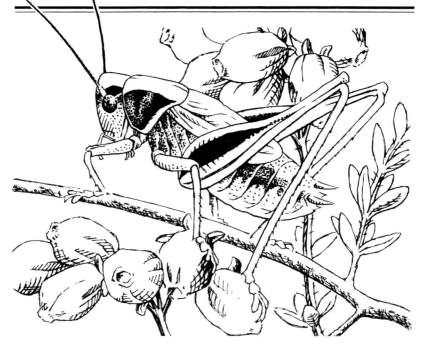

BOG BUSH-CRICKET
Metrioptera brachyptera (L.)

There are two colour forms: one is almost entirely brown, except for the underside of the abdomen, which is bright green; the other form differs in that it has green markings on the wings, hind femora and dorsal surfaces of the head and pronotum. Adults attain a total length of about 15 mm. The wings are reduced to short flaps except in a very rare macropterous form. There is a conspicuous pale band along the posterior margin of the side of the pronotum (fig. 16b). The ovipositor is longer and straighter than that of Roesel's Bush-cricket. The song which has been described as a monotonous chuffing is a reliable sign of its presence. It may be heard from late July to October.

In Britain, *M. brachyptera* seems almost always to be associated with heather, especially with the cross-leaved heath. It is fond of sitting amongst the heather. In Berkshire it occurs on several heaths between Newbury and the Surrey border, where localities include Burghfield Common and Owlsmoor. The rare macropterous form has been recorded from Wellington College and Burghfield Common. In Buckinghamshire, where suitable habitat is scarce, this insect is known from East

43

Burnham Common and Stoke Common. There is no recent Oxfordshire record.

In fact, the Bog Bush-cricket serves as a very useful marker of high quality heathland habitat in our area. Wherever it occurs, one should expect to find a good selection of other choice heathland plants and animals. In Berkshire this bush-cricket coexists with many desirable insects, including: Silver-studded Blue butterfly and Grayling butterfly, the Black darter dragonfly, *Sympetrum danae* and the local ants, *Tetramorium caespitum* and *Formica sanguinea.*

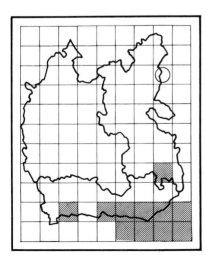
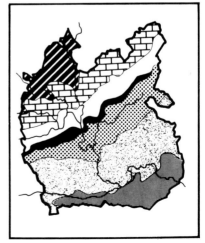

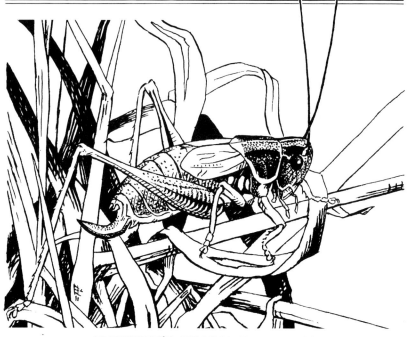

ROESEL'S BUSH-CRICKET
Metrioptera roeselii (Hagenbach)

Roesel's Bush-cricket is about 15 mm long, predominantly brown in colour with some yellowish-green markings. There is a conspicuous pale band along the anterior and posterior margins of the sides of the pronotum (fig 16a). The ovipositor is short and upcurved. Typical specimens have short, flap-like wings. Many macropterous specimens were noted during the hot summer of 1984. The song is a loud continuous buzzing noise which may be heard from late July to late September.

During the early part of the century, *M. roeselii* was a rare insect in Britain which entomologists regarded as being something of a prize. Lucas (1920) writes that '. . . this species is confined to the south-east coast of England, and till a few years ago was almost lost to sight.' The majority of records were from dunes and salt-marshes in Kent, Essex and Lincolnshire. Roesel's Bush-cricket was subsequently recorded from several other counties and over the last decade seems to have made a considerable expansion in its range of distribution. During the 1980s it became widespread on waste ground throughout Greater London and was added to the Berkshire list by Mr. R. Williams. It was still present at this site (a railway embankment west of Maidenhead) in 1986. Its discovery in Buckinghamshire might be anticipated. In 1988, the author found this insect in abundance along roadside verges in the Watford district of Greater London where localities included a slip road of the M25 motorway. At Watford, as in many other of this insect's British localities, Roesel's Bush-cricket was found in association with the Essex Skipper butterfly. Both species of insect seem able to exploit the opportunities provided by the grassy margins of new road systems which might be expected to facilitate the spread of these attractive species into the three counties.

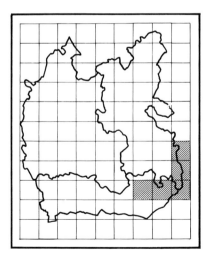
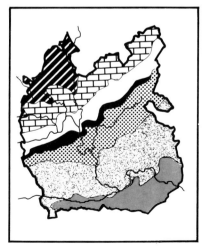

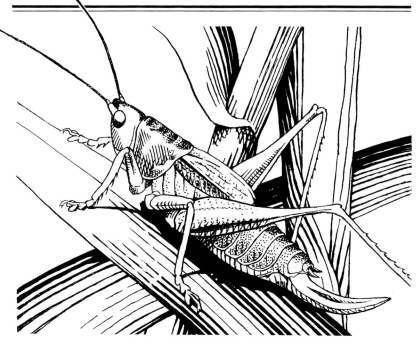

SHORT-WINGED CONEHEAD
Conocephalus dorsalis (Latreille)

Identification presents no difficulty with *C. dorsalis* in our region. Being a rather dainty species a little over 1 cm in length with a conical head shape and a broad brown median stripe there is no other species with which it could be confused. The ovipositor is upcurved. The wings are vestigial and unsuitable for flight, except in a very rare macropterous form *burri* Ebner. Near the south coast, there is a similar species, the Long-winged Conehead, *C. discolor*, with long wings and a straighter ovipositor.

The song of *C. dorsalis* alternates between a ticking phase and a soft rustling noise. Unfortunately, the song is usually inaudible to older ears being composed of high frequencies. Even younger persons may experience difficulty hearing it on a windy day amongst the reeds and sedges of the marshes that this insect frequents, when this insect's stridulation sounds like little more than a whisper against the clamour of the wind through the vegetation. The season for adults lasts from late July to late October. *C. dorsalis* is to be sought amongst sedges or long grass in marshes and bogs. They cling to the stems and step round to the far side of the stem with great agility when disturbed by an observer. Hence, they are tricky to photograph and harder to catch. One moderately effective means of collecting a specimen is to slap one's hollowed palms together so that the insect becomes trapped in the space between the two hands, whilst still clinging to a stem.

The distribution in Britain is mainly coastal (salt-marshes and marram hills) but there are numerous inland localities (fens, bogs and water meadows). This species is reputed to occur by the Thames in the Runnymede district on the Berkshire/Surrey border. Furthermore, *C. dorsalis* is recorded from peat bogs in Surrey and is quite likely to be present on similar terrain in Berkshire. There is no reliable, recent record from the Oxford district, but there is a male preserved in the Hope Collections, Oxford with data: 'Tubney, J. Collins, Aug. 1911', and one hopes that it might be rediscovered.

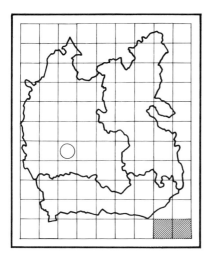 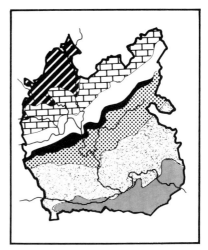

SPECKLED BUSH-CRICKET
Leptophyes punctatissima (Bosc)

Speckled Bush-crickets are green with tiny speckled markings and are about 12 mm long. The wings are vestigial in the male and scarcely visible as such in the female. Females have a very bulky appearance. Males have a brown dorsal stripe which may be faint or well marked. The song consists of very quiet ticks. Nymphs seem to be more active and numerous than adults and may be seen in May or June. Adults are fond of basking on nettles and brambles and occur from late July till late September.

Speckled Bush-crickets favour low bushes and nettles on the edges of woods and along hedges. They frequently colonise roses and other shrubs in gardens where insecticides are not used. In late summer, specimens are frequently spotted on walls and fences where they are very conspicuous. They are at least partly carnivorous. It is easy to introduce this species to a reasonably scrubby garden, if not already present.

This species may also be found in reedbeds, saltmarshes and fens (such as the valley fen at Wick Copse) and when in such habitat males might be mistaken for Short-winged Conehead, *C. dorsalis.* However, Speckled Bush-crickets are less nimble and have tiny speckles.

There must be few, if any, 10 km squares in Berkshire, Buckinghamshire and Oxfordshire which lack this species. Localities near Oxford include: Parsonage Moor, Wick Copse, Whitecross Green Wood, Wychwood Forest, Oakley Wood and the grounds of the John Radcliffe Hospital.

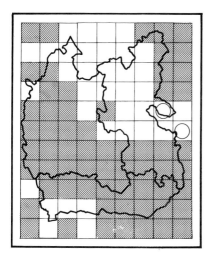 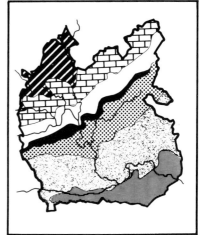

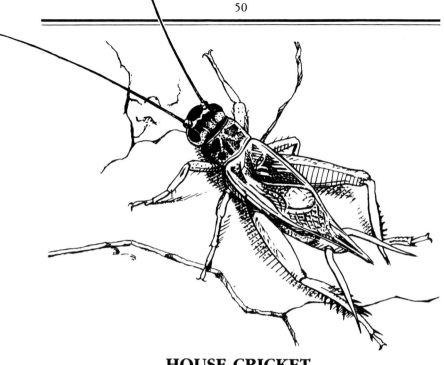

HOUSE CRICKET
Acheta domesticus (L.)

House crickets are no longer generally encountered in houses. However, they are still quite widespread in older British hospitals and also occur sporadically in new hospitals. These insects are widely used as laboratory animals for experiments and as a food source for larger carnivorous insects and as a consequence populations of this insect are sometimes found in the vicinity of biology laboratories. Rubbish dumps can support colonies of the house cricket, especially during the warmer months. During hot summers, house crickets are able to extend their range into the outdoor world and individuals can be heard stridulating some distance from the nearest building. House crickets can also be heard outdoors in the middle of winter close to the outlets of hospital ventilation ducts, the heaters being permanently in operation at that time of the year. There is no evidence to suggest that house crickets pose any particular threat to health.

House crickets are more often heard than seen. The song consists of repeated shrill chirps, whose persistence may be a source of considerable irritation to those present at night on a Victorian hospital ward in the presence of a stridulating male. The song may be so repetitive as to cause the listener to mistake it for the sound of faulty machinery. Nevertheless, for those naturalists who seldom encounter the species, the song of the house cricket is a source of delight.

Adults are quite large with a total body length of about 15 mm. They are yellowish brown or grey with additional dark markings and fully developed wings. Since this species frequents permanently heated buildings, all stages of the life-cycle may be present at any given moment. Nymphs are pale brown and wingless. The natural home of this insect is possibly North Africa, but it is now of cosmopolitan distribution and has probably been resident in Britain for several centuries.

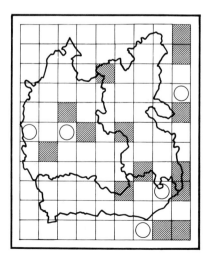
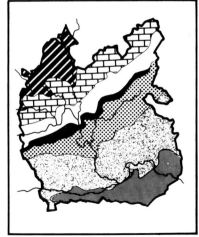

MOLE CRICKET
Gryllotalpa gryllotalpa (L.)

Mole crickets are of unmistakable appearance, adults being large (35–45 mm) and bulky with spadelike forelimbs adapted to burrowing. Nymphs resemble adults but are smaller and lack wings. Imagines have well-developed wings and are capable of flight in hot weather. The general colour is brown.

Mole crickets spend much of their lives underground in tunnels in a manner similar to that of moles. They are partly vegetarian and may cause damage to crops. The male constructs a special burrow the entrance of which is modified to form a sounding chamber from which he emits his monotonous call in the spring. The lifespan is long, lasting about two and a half years.

Sadly, this insect is now so rare in Britain that it is feared to be on the verge of extinction. The most recent British mainland records have been from lowland sites near the south coast in the Bournemouth and Southampton districts. There is an old record from Besselsleigh west of Oxford. It still occurs in Guernsey. There is a possibility that the species might be imported amongst root vegetables from abroad as it is a pest in some countries. It is a protected species in Britain.

Mole Crickets are widespread around the warmer parts of the world and most species are superficially very similar. Some species of the genus *Gryllotalpa* appear to be anatomically identical but have different geographical ranges and songs. Two species found in southern Europe (one of which is our *G. gryllotalpa*) can only be separated with confidence by determining their chromosome numbers.

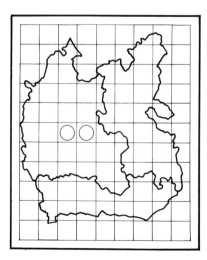

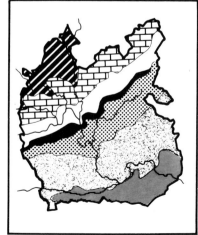

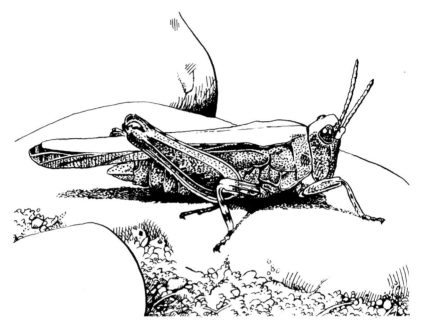

SLENDER GROUNDHOPPER
Tetrix subulata (L.)

Two species of groundhopper occur in our region, *Tetrix subulata* and
T. undulata. The third British species, *T. ceperoi*, which closely
resembles *T. subulata* is confined to coastal districts. There are two
forms of the Slender Groundhopper: the typical one in which the
pronotum extends well beyond the hind knees and a rarer form
(*f.bifasciata* Herbst) in which the pronotum is short, causing the insect to
resemble *T. undulata*. However, in both forms of *T. subulata*, the dorsal
surface of the pronotum is almost flat, whereas in *T. undulata* there is
a prominent raised median keel (fig 13). Unfortunately, final instar
nymphs of *T. subulata* have a raised median keel and much resemble *T.
undulata*. Such nymphs may be kept alive (as described on page 22) till
adulthood. The general coloration is brown or grey, sometimes with a
pale dorsal stripe. Some individuals are reddish, buff or tinged with
green. Groundhoppers do not stridulate.

    Adults of all the British groundhoppers hibernate and become active
and mate in April. April and May are the best months in which to seek
adults. They are good swimmers and fly in hot weather. Nymphs may be

found during the summer. They attain adulthood during August and September.

The Slender Groundhopper frequents damp mud on the banks of streams, ponds and rivers where they appear to feed mainly on algae. More rarely they may be found in dry leaf litter in woodland.

This species is probably more widespread than records suggest. Localities include: Ot Moor, Ruskin Reserve Cothill, Dry Sandford Pit, Wychwood Forest, Bullingdon Bog, Tubney, Blackthorn, Whitecross Green Wood and Bernwood Forest. It is locally common on the banks of the river Thames from upstream at Radcot (and also across the Gloucestershire border at Lechlade) downstream to the Runnymede district, where Berkshire meets Surrey. This insect inhabits water meadows by the Cherwell, a short distance from the centre of Oxford.

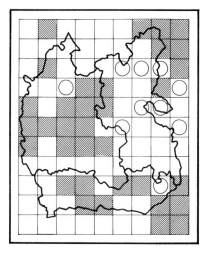
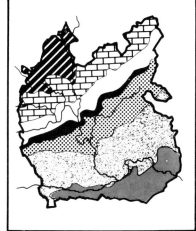

COMMON GROUNDHOPPER
Tetrix undulata Sowerby

Guidance on the identification of our groundhoppers is given in the section covering the previous species. *T. undulata* is a robust species with a prominent median keel along the dorsum of the pronotum (fig 13). The general coloration is brown with various dark markings. The seasonal pattern of the life-cycle is not so well defined as that of the previous species: adults and nymphs hibernate and adults may be found throughout the year, although they seem to be most numerous in April and May.

The range of habitat favoured by this species includes heathland, bogs, woodland, downland and river banks. It is usually to be found on the ground rather like a game-bird sitting low amongst heather:*Tetrix* means 'grouse' in Greek.

In April 1987, the author collected an adult specimen of this species at Watlington Hill in which the pronotum was reduced in length so as to reveal the entire upper surface of the abdomen and wings. It is presumed that this insect suffered some accident at the time of one of its moults to become deformed as described. Such examples would lack the key character of an extended pronotum and must be very rare.

There are numerous localities for this species including: Wasing and Owlsmoor in Berkshire; Buttler's Hangings, Turville, Rushbeds Wood, Shabbington Wood and Stoke Common in Buckinghamshire; Tubney, Stanton Great Wood, Waterperry Wood, Bladon Heath, Wytham Wood, Wychwood Forest, Watlington Hill and Warren Bank in Oxfordshire.

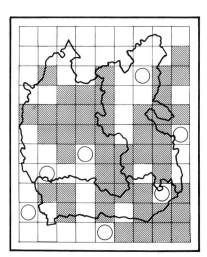
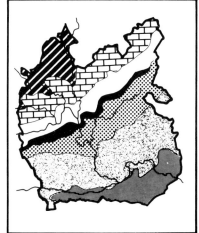

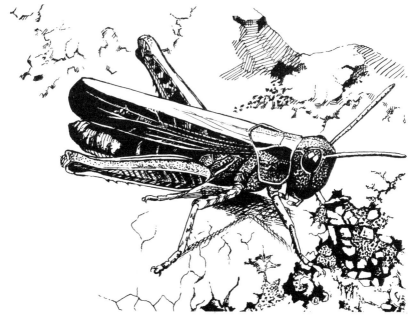

WOODLAND GRASSHOPPER
Omocestus rufipes Zett.

Mature examples of this species are easily identified: the general coloration of both sexes is usually dark brown, although the wings and dorsal surface of the pronotum may be green in some females; the palps are conspicuously white; the underside of the thorax is smooth; the tip of the abdomen is bright red. The song consists of a series of ticking sounds and lasts for about 5–10 seconds; it is rather like the song of its congener, the Common Green Grasshopper but is less prolonged.

One finds this grasshopper in or near the edges of woodland. In our region the Common Green Grasshopper is often found in the same locality as the Woodland Grasshopper. In Bernwood Forest, the Woodland Grasshopper seems to be confined to a number of cross-rides where it favours sunny clearings with patches of bare earth, scattered pine needles and tufts of grass. In contrast, the Common Green is to be heard on all the rides, especially where they are well grassed over. Both species of *Omocestus* are absent from neglected woodland which lacks the light gaps provided by well-maintained rides and coppice. In its Berkshire localities, *O. rufipes* may be seen on rides in young conifer plantations and amongst bracken in large clearings. The Woodland Grasshopper occurs in woodland clearings on chalk hills as well as on acidic heathy woodland borders.

O. rufipes is a rarity in the three counties and may have died out in some of its old localities, which include Rammamere Heath in Buckinghamshire and Bladon Heath and Bagley Wood in Oxfordshire, but lack of specimens from some localities does introduce the possibility of previous confusion with the Common Green and hinders the assessment of old records. Furthermore, it is possible that colonies might be rediscovered at these sites. It occurs in Bernwood Forest on both sides of the Buckinghamshire/Oxfordshire border. This species has been reported from wooded parts of the Oxfordshire Chilterns, including the Warburg Reserve at Bix Bottom. In Berkshire, it occurs at Burghfield Common and in Windsor Great Park. There is no recent British record for this insect from areas north of Bernwood Forest, although it is a common species in many parts of Hampshire and Sussex and in Europe it has an extensive distribution including southern Sweden and southern Greece.

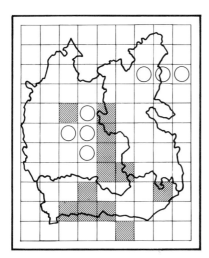
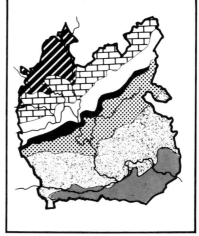

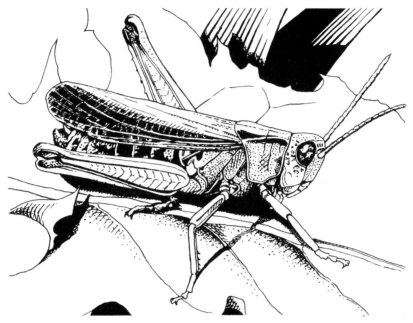

COMMON GREEN GRASSHOPPER
Omocestus viridulus (L.)

As one might expect, the majority of specimens of *O. viridulus* are bright green. Mature adult males can be separated into forms which are either all green or all brown. Brown forms of the male sometimes have a yellowish tinge. Females are always at least partly green and frequently entirely green in colour. Those females which bear other pigmentation, have it restricted to the sides of the body and to a narrow dorsal medial stripe on the head and pronotum. Some of these dichromic females look very dark, with chocolate coloured sides; in others the sides and dorsal stripe are straw coloured. There is a very rare form, seen only in females, in which the sides of the body are of a beautiful pinkish purple. There is also a purple, median, dorsal stripe in this form; the rest of the dorsal surface being green. The undersurface of the body is smooth. The pronotum is as shown in fig 11b. The calling song of the male is a distinctive, loud ticking sound which lasts for 15–20 seconds but may last for over a minute during courtship. This is the earliest grasshopper to mature: in a hot season it may be mature by the first week of June. Adults may be heard as late as October.

Upland Britain has the strongest populations of this species where it is common on rough pastures and heaths even at high altitude. In dry lowlands, strong colonies can sometimes be seen to occur in fens, where the surrounding arable land and dry pasture lack this insect. In our region it may be found on the Chilterns, Cotswolds and Berkshire Downs, as well as other areas of semi-natural grassland. It is common along the grassy rides of some woods as is the case in Bernwood Forest, where it is the most common grasshopper on many of the rides. It also occurs on commons and heaths such as Bucklebury Common in Berkshire. Sites near Oxford include Waterperry Wood, Whitecross Green Wood, Shabbington Wood, Hell Coppice, Wytham Wood, Parsonage Moor and Shotover. In fact, this grasshopper is widespread in the three counties but is much more localised than the Common Field and Meadow Grasshoppers.

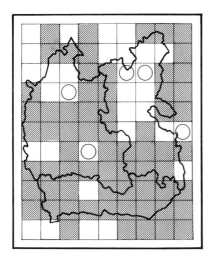
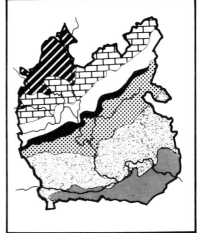

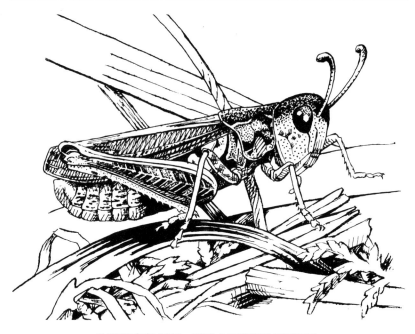

MOTTLED GRASSHOPPER
Myrmeleotettix maculatus (Thunberg)

The Mottled Grasshopper is the smallest species of Acridid known in mainland Britain. Males are generally smaller than females. The antennae are obviously clubbed in both sexes, especially in the male. The only other species in our region with clubbed antennae is the Rufous Grasshopper, in which the antennae are tipped with white. The side-keels of the pronotum of the Mottled Grasshopper are strongly incurved. There are numerous colour varieties, often with contrasting patterns of grey, black, green or purple and it is a laborious procedure to separate them into distinct forms. The song has a rough, wheezy quality and may be heard from June to October. *M. maculatus* seems to require well-drained sites with thin, exposed soils and is often found in association with the Grayling butterfly, *Eumenes semele*. This grasshopper frequents heaths and chalk or limestone grassland. In other regions it may also be found on dunes, moors and old slag heaps. It has a wide but localised distribution in the British Isles being found in such varied parts of the country as the machair of the Outer Hebrides, the clifftop heaths of Cornwall and the abandoned slag heaps of the English midlands.

The Mottled Grasshopper is scarce in our region. It occurs at Wychwood, Buckland Warren, Taynton Quarry, Wytham Hill and Hitchcopse Pit in Oxfordshire; on the steeper Chiltern slopes (e.g. Watlington Hill) and some Berkshire heaths such as Owlsmoor and in the Burghfield Common area. The colonies of this grasshopper at Wychwood and Wytham appear to be highly localised. The Wychwood site, which has been examined by John Campbell of Woodstock museum, consists of a tiny area of crumbling limestone by the side of a lake in what is otherwise moist woodland, devoid of suitable habitat for this species. The Mottled Grasshopper shares this precarious locality with the Brown Argus butterfly. At Wytham Wood, this species seems to be restricted to a small rabbit-grazed clearing where the Common Groundhopper also occurs. There are many specimens of the Mottled Grasshopper in the Hope Entomological Collections which were collected at Tubney and Frilford Heath before the area became a golf course. Clearly the species once abounded there and it is possible that small populations still exist on the fragments of heath that persist on the golf course. To observe strong colonies one should visit steep, well-grazed Chiltern slopes or the heathlands that remain along the borders of Berkshire, Hampshire and Surrey.

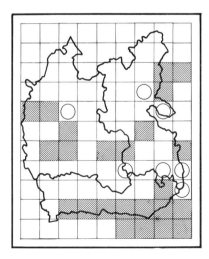
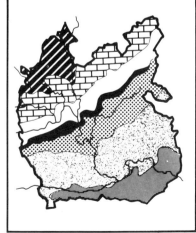

RUFOUS GRASSHOPPER
Gomphocerippus rufus (L.)

The male Rufous Grasshopper cannot be mistaken as its antennae are strongly clubbed and conspicuously tipped with white; those of the female are similar, although the degree of clubbing is less marked. Both sexes are of a warm brown colour, although one sometimes sees paler, chalk-coloured individuals and a rare purple variety has been described. Whilst in some the colouring is homogeneous, others show a pale dorsal stripe and black wedge marks on the pronotum. In most specimens, the wings do not quite reach beyond the hind knees and in gravid females the tip of the abdomen may protrude well past the wings. The chirp is of a rustling nature, lasting several seconds.

Herb-rich calcareous downland is the habitat of this grasshopper and its detection at such a site is highly indicative that the same site would yield downland orchids and Chalkhill Blue butterflies. The best sites are along woodland borders and it has been found sheltering under leaves in cold weather. This habit may explain its persisting later in the season than other grasshoppers. The first adults are seen in late July and August and in Sussex have been recorded as late as December.

This is a local insect in our region, apparently confined to the south-facing slopes between Goring and Mapledurham in Oxfordshire. Its reputed occurrence in Berkshire may be based on specimens in the Hope Collections with data: 'Hardwick, Reading, Aug 1896, H.R. Smith', which locality is in Oxfordshire. It is locally common in the Cotswolds in Gloucestershire and may yet be found on the Oxfordshire oolite.

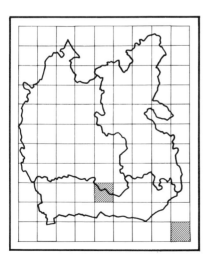
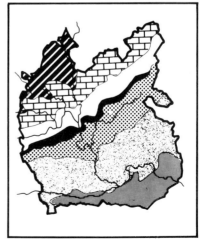

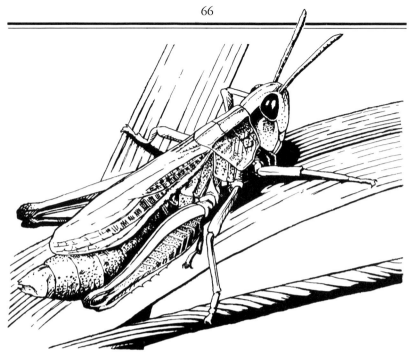

LESSER MARSH GRASSHOPPER
Chorthippus albomarginatus (Degeer)

The side-keels of the pronotum are nearly parallel. The pronotum lacks markings. The wings are longer than in *Ch. parallelus* but fail to reach the hind knees. Unlike those of *Ch. parallelus*, the hind knees of the male are not usually conspicuously brown. As with most other Orthoptera, the female is larger than the male. There is often a white stripe along the anterior margin of the forewings. The general colour is usually a combination of green or brown. Some specimens are almost entirely brown or entirely green or are green with brown hind legs. Some have brown or reddish pigment on the dorsal surface of the body with green sides whilst others have the opposite combination of a green back and brown sides. The proportion of these various colour forms seems to vary from one colony to another. Isolated males produce short quiet chirps. This species is often found in large congregations of both sexes where the courtship songs of the males produce a loud chorus. Mature adults may be heard from mid-July to late September.

The usual habitat consists of low-lying meadows, especially where there are clumps of sedge, *Carex* spp. It also occurs in damp clearings in woods. On the Oxfordshire/Warwickshire border *Ch. albomarginatus* has been found amongst gorse on dry hill tops. Elsewhere in Britain it is found in saltmarshes and on sand-dunes.

There are probably many localities yet to be discovered in the three counties. Most records from our region are from Oxfordshire where sites include: Rough Hill near Epwell, Bladon Heath, Binsey, Ot Moor and Whitecross Green Wood. There are old specimens in the Hope Collections from Cowley Marsh. In Buckinghamshire it occurs in Bernwood Forest and in a field next to Rushbeds Wood. There is an old record from Crookham Common, near Newbury, Berkshire.

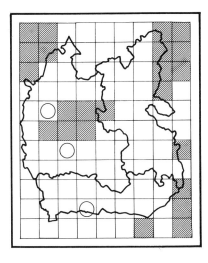
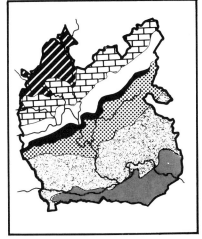

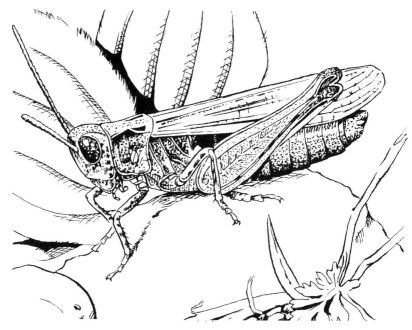

COMMON FIELD GRASSHOPPER
Chorthippus brunneus (Thunberg)

This is a fairly large species with long wings which extend well beyond the hind knees, a conspicuously downy underside of the thorax and a characteristically shaped pronotum (fig 6c). The majority of specimens are brown in colour with mottled or striped patterns. Some are almost uniform in colour whilst others show contrasting patterns of light and dark pigment. Nymphs which grow on dark scorched earth, such as that which occurs after heath fires, may acquire large amounts of dark pigment to produce adults that are almost black in colour. The end of the abdomen is reddish in the mature male. There is a number of beautiful colour varieties. Some examples are completely pink or buff in colour; others have green wings and green upper surfaced pronota. A splendid and very rare form which is completely green but for the wings is occasionally reported: the author captured such an example of a female in September 1986 at Lough Down, Berkshire.

This grasshopper thrives on ground which has been disturbed by man's activities: it is common on roadside verges, on derelict ground in cities, in railway cuttings and in old quarries. In hot weather they are very mobile and may move into gardens or into the middle of city carparks where they enjoy basking on the hot tarmac. Thus, it is perhaps our most noticed grasshopper, rather as the House Sparrow is perceived as being our most common bird. The Common Field Grasshopper also occurs in many semi-natural habitats — heaths, downland, woodland rides and fields. On lusher stretches of downland, this species may be localised to anthills or places where the ground has been disturbed by the burrowing of rabbits or foxes. The females make use of such exposed ground for basking and egg-laying. Adults may be heard from early July till November. The song consists of a series of short, subdued chirps.

If searched for, this insect would probably be located in every 10 km square of our region. Localities are too numerous to mention.

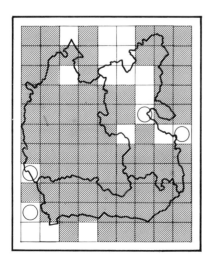
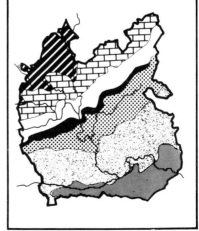

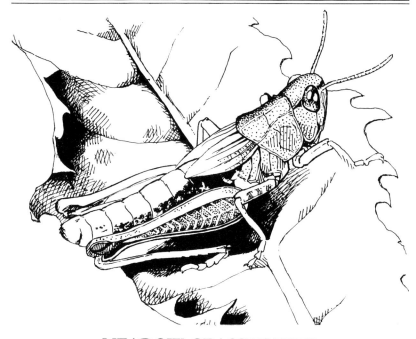

MEADOW GRASSHOPPER
Chorthippus parallelus (Zetterstedt)

The typical form of this species is easy to identify. The side-keels of the pronotum are gently incurved (fig 6b). In males the wings fail to reach the hind knees which are conspicuously brown. The wings of the female are much reduced and are quite useless for flight. Most specimens are brown or green but there are also purple varieties. One beautiful form of the female is almost entirely purple in colour. The dorsal surface of the pronotum of this species is often uniform in colour, especially in green varieties. Brown specimens in particular may exhibit contrasting dark stripes and wedges on the pronotum. In seasons and places of exceptional abundance, a rare macropterous form, f. *explicatus* (Selys), of both sexes may be observed. The wings extend beyond the hind knees and both sexes of this form have the power of flight. There is some resemblance of this form to the Lesser Marsh Grasshopper, but f. *explicatus* has wings which extend beyond the hind knees (which are brown) and the side-keels are more strongly incurved. The chirp, which is often repeated many times, lasts several seconds and may be heard from July till November.

The Meadow Grasshopper may be found on most types of grassland, on damp heaths, woodland rides, waste ground and roadside verges.

If searched for this insect would probably be found in every 10 km square in our region. This insect is one of our most common species of Orthoptera.

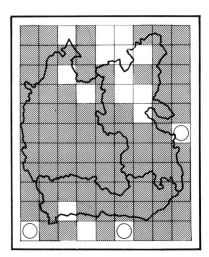
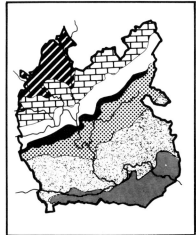

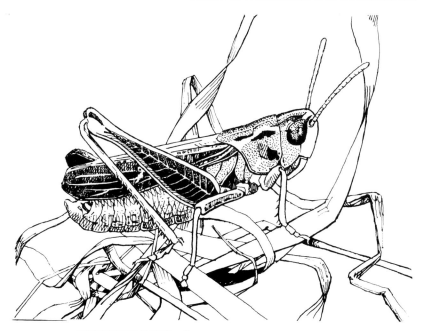

STRIPE-WINGED GRASSHOPPER
Stenobothrus lineatus (Panzer)

Perhaps the most distinguishing feature of this grasshopper is the wavering, wheezy song of the isolated male. This sound is unlike that of any other British grasshopper. During courtship, the male produces a ticking song, rather like the song of an isolated Common Green but quieter. In the majority of specimens, the general coloration is glossy green with green pigment covering the greater part of the pronotum, forewings and legs. Some predominantly green individuals have brown or purple hind legs. It is unusual to see any purple colour in this species. Rarely the wings and dorsal surface of the pronotum are brown. The male has reddish hind tibiae and a well defined *stigma* (see fig 10). Females usually have a bright *linea scapularis* (see fig 10). Some colour forms possess a *stria postulnaris* (see fig 10). The ovipositor of the female is distinctive (see fig 11a) and furthermore the wing venation is distinctive (see fig 9b).

The usual habitat of this species is short, downland turf on chalk or other types of limestone. In such habitat it is often to be found in association with the Chalkhill Blue butterfly, *Lysandra coridon*. In other parts of the country, including Surrey and the adjacent part of Berkshire, it has been found on dry, sandy heaths. Adults may be found from late July to the end of September.

Localities on chalk include: Watlington Hill, Goring, Turville Hill and other sites in the Oxfordshire and Buckinghamshire Chilterns; also Whitehorse Hill and Lough Down in Berkshire. At Silwood Park and Windsor Great Park, Berkshire, populations of this insect exist on sandy terrain. It is common in Gloucestershire at places on the oolitic limestone and might be discovered in similar localities in West Oxfordshire.

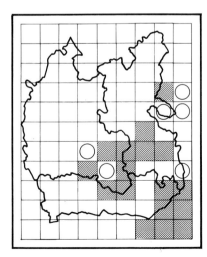
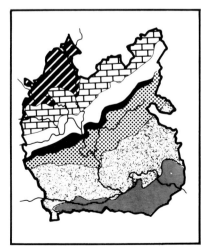

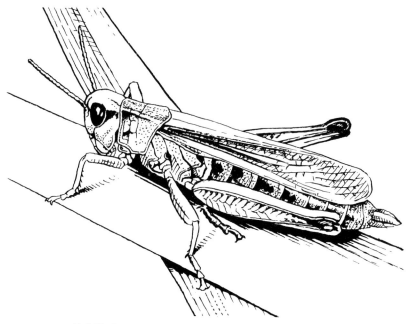

LARGE MARSH GRASSHOPPER
Stethophyma grossum (L.)

Being by far the largest British Grasshopper — females attaining a length of about 3 cm — adults cannot be mistaken. Identification is further aided by the presence of broad yellow and black rings around the hind tibiae. The body surface is smooth and glossy and the usual coloration consists of some combination of brown and green. Rarely, purple forms occur. The song is distinctive, being composed of a series of loud, well-spaced ticks. The season for adults lasts from August till November.

S. grossum is a rarity in the British Isles, records from the 1980s being limited to the bogs of the New Forest, Dorset, Somerset, Surrey and western Ireland. It seems to have become extinct in East Anglia and the London district. Its reputed occurrence in Berkshire in the past is not supported by known specimens, although its recent discovery at a new locality on M.O.D. land in Surrey, a few miles from the Berkshire border, would seem to support the notion that it might once have occurred in Berkshire.

Although there is a faint hope that this species might be discovered on one of the few remaining Berkshire bogs, the best place to see this species in England is the New Forest. There it is locally common and may be seen on hot days in late summer in many of the bogs. It is most common in the middle of quaking bogs, where there is cotton grass and bog myrtle. Exploration of such localities requires the utmost caution: there is a danger of sinking into the bog and furthermore adders are often present amongst the drier patches of vegetation.

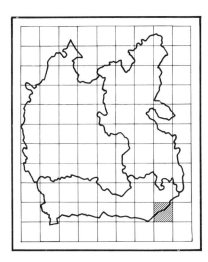
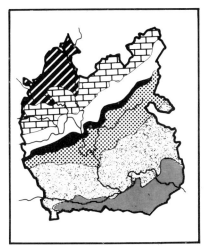

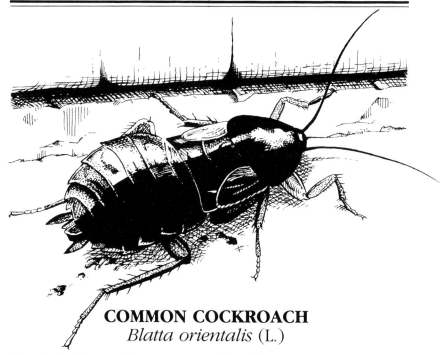

COMMON COCKROACH
Blatta orientalis (L.)

The original home of the Common Cockroach is uncertain. Africa seems the most probable place of origin, although outdoor populations in Crimea suggest a possible Asiatic homeland. The Common Cockroach dispersed northwards into the human habitations of Europe long ago. Moffet records it in England in the early 1600s, whilst Gilbert White describes the insect at Selborne in the late 1700s. This insect can now be found in association with man throughout the British Isles. It is probably widespread in the three counties and is locally common in certain parts of Oxford.

Typical habitat includes kitchens and basements of larger, older institutions, such as hospitals, museums and universities. A survey published in the Journal of Hospital Infection (1981.2:5–9) records this insect from 57 out of 93 British hospitals. It occurs in some new buildings and also outdoors on rubbish dumps. The species prefers relatively cool conditions (20–28°C), is nocturnal and may take a year to reach the adult state. It is a large cockroach (20–24 mm long). The females are wingless and dark brown or almost black in colour. The males are brown with forewings which do not reach the tip of the abdomen. The species is quite sluggish in its movements compared with our other pest species.

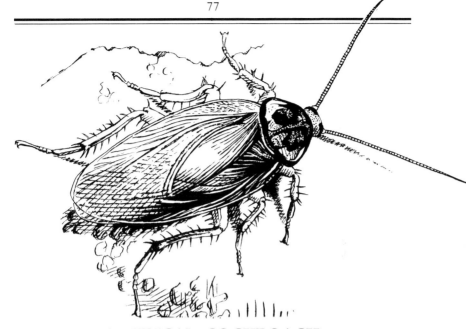

AMERICAN COCKROACH
Periplaneta americana (L.)

Although the American Cockroach does not appear to have been reported as a pest species in the three counties, it is included here because it is the species of cockroach which is most widely used in schools and universities for teaching insect anatomy and as an experimental animal. Therefore, the reader is likely to be familiar with it. Furthermore, this insect is so common abroad and in other parts of the British Isles that odd specimens must be imported to our region from time to time.

It is a large insect, 3–4 cm in length, rich red-brown in colour with well developed wings. There is an ill-defined dark area on the pronotum. Both sexes are similar in appearance. Nymphs are reddish or golden-brown in colour and undergo a variable number of moults before reaching adulthood.

A high temperature is required for development (c. 30°C) so the American Cockroach in Britain can thrive only in permanently heated buildings, such as hospitals and botanical hot houses. When kept as a laboratory animal it sometimes escapes to set up colonies in the vicinity of the laboratory. Despite its name, the American Cockroach probably originated in Africa.

AUSTRALIAN COCKROACH
Periplaneta australasiae (Fabricius)

This insect is superficially similar to the American Cockroach but is smaller (c. 3 cm) and usually darker in colour. There is a well-defined dark mark on the pronotum surrounded by a yellow band. There is a yellow band on the anterior margin of the forewings. The two sexes are similar.

As is the case with the American Cockroach, high temperatures are required for the maintenance of a colony. Such conditions existed in a hot house in Headington, Oxford, earlier this century, where a population occurred, but there does not appear to be a recent Oxfordshire record. Visitors to Kew Gardens have the opportunity of seeing this species in at least one of the heated plant houses. This insect sometimes arrives amongst imported goods.

Many of the cosmopolitan, pest species of cockroach, including the Australian Cockroach appear to have originated in Africa.

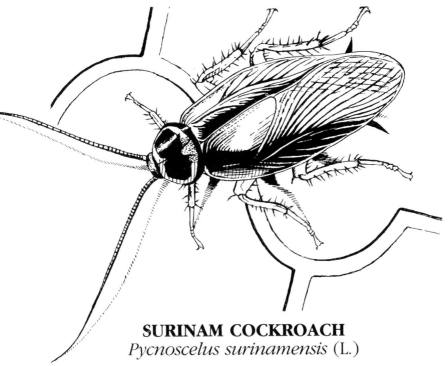

SURINAM COCKROACH
Pycnoscelus surinamensis (L.)

Whilst Surinam is in South America, it is thought that this insect originated in Asia. It is of moderate size (total length about 2 cm) dark brown in colour, with fully developed wings. The pronotum is dark with a pale anterior margin. Reproduction is by parthenogenesis and males are very rare except in south-east Asia.

Heated greenhouses provide a habitat for this insect in Britain and there is an old record from a hot house at Thame Park, Oxfordshire. It is destructive to plants and Lucas (1920) quotes that it is '. . . most pernicious to pines' but that it is '. . . of very elegant proportions, and will not disgrace the orthopterist's cabinet.'

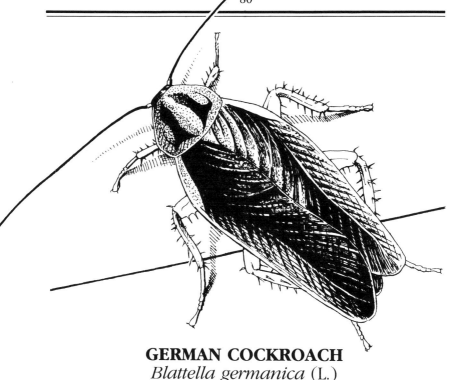

GERMAN COCKROACH
Blattella germanica (L.)

The German Cockroach probably originated in Africa, but by the time of Linnaeus it had become established in northern Europe. Amongst the British indoor pest species of cockroach it is the next most common after the Common Cockroach, *Blatta orientalis*. It is a small species (total length about 12 mm), pale brown in colour, with paired dark stripes on the pronotum and well developed wings. Males and females are similar.

In Britain, this insect requires permanently warm buildings and is able to thrive in such places as hospital kitchens. Like other pest cockroaches it is mainly nocturnal and may be difficult to detect during the day.

At the start of this century this species was recorded from the Randolph Hotel kitchen in Oxford, but there is no recent record from that site. Older hospitals seem to be the most fruitful places to search for this species in Britain today.

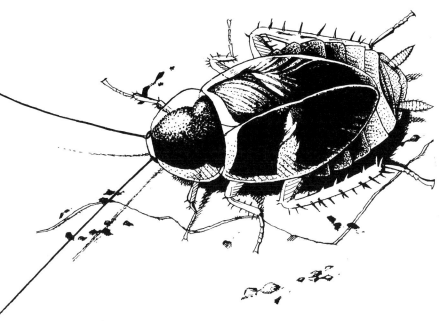

BROWN-BANDED COCKROACH
Supella longipalpa (Fabricius)

In 1965, the Brown-banded Cockroach was known to be breeding in only two British counties: Devon and Greater London. Since then it has spread to many other areas and it is probable that colonies will become established in the three counties, if this has not already happened.

Males are about 13 mm long and possess wings which extend beyond the tip of the abdomen. The pronotum has a dark central area. Females are about 10 mm long with wings which do not reach the tip of the abdomen. The general colour of females is darker brown than that of males. Both sexes have two pale stripes which cross the wings perpendicular to the body axis.

Unlike the other pest cockroaches in Britain, which tend to be limited to the damper, darker recesses of a building, the Brown-banded readily colonises comparatively hygienic areas, including clean, modern kitchens, provided that there is a constant source of warmth.

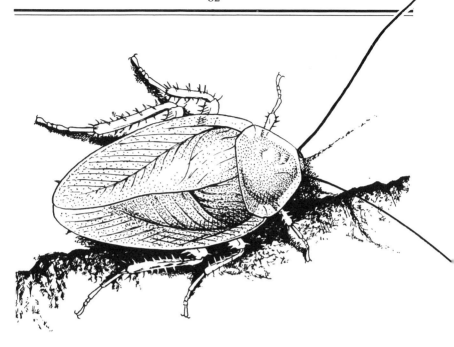

TAWNY COCKROACH
Ectobius pallidus (Olivier)

Both sexes of this delicate little cockroach are very similar in appearance, being 8–9 mm in length, yellow-brown in colour, with fully developed wings. Males have a glandular hollow, which contains no tubercle, in the seventh abdominal segment. Females lack such specialisation of the seventh segment and may be found carrying an ootheca. The ootheca is brown in colour and is carried for several days before being deposited.

Like its congener, the Dusky Cockroach, this insect has a two year life cycle. Nymphs hatch in the spring and reach the final nymphal instar by autumn when they hibernate. During the following spring such nymphs moult to become adults. Breeding takes place during the summer and resulting oothecae overwinter.

Suitable habitats for this cockroach include: heathland, woodland clearings, dunes and rough places on cliffs. They may be seen running over the ground or vegetation. Where the species is common specimens can be obtained by searching through clumps of dried grass or by lifting up the overhanging stems of heathers.

As a British insect, the Tawny Cockroach shows a strong bias for the south coast. It is locally abundant in such places as the New Forest and Isle of Purbeck. In the three counties, this insect is near the northern limit of its British range. It occurs in woods and heaths of southern Berkshire. Burghfield Common is one of its localities.

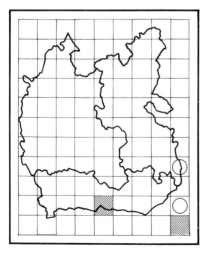
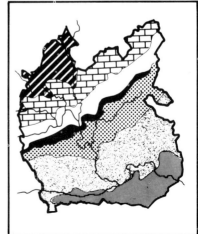

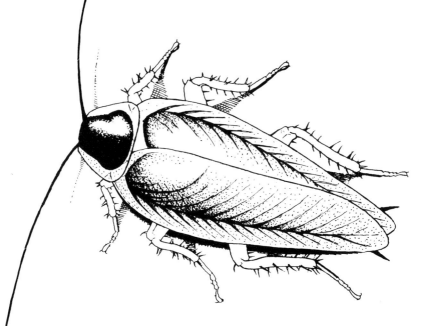

DUSKY COCKROACH
Ectobius lapponicus (L.)

This dainty insect is slightly larger than the Tawny Cockroach, females being about 9 mm long and males being 10–11 mm in length. Males are slender and grey in colour, usually with a large dark mark or with paired dark markings on the pronotum. In males the wings extend beyond the tip of the abdomen. There is a tubercle in the glandular hollow. Females resemble the Tawny Cockroach in general outline but they are darker in colour and the wings do not reach the tip of the abdomen.

Nymphs undergo their final moult in the spring and adults may be seen from late May till October. Oothecae deposited during the summer do not hatch till the following spring. This species exists as a nymph for about one year of its two year life cycle.

The Dusky Cockroach is active in hot weather and may be seen running over vegetation, resting on tips of stems and sometimes flying. Nymphs can be found on the underside of pieces of discarded cardboard. Habitat includes heaths, woods and chalk downland.

In Britain, the range of distribution is limited to the southern counties where it is common in parts of Sussex and Hampshire. Localities in the three counties include: Wasing, Aldermaston and Sunningdale in Berkshire and Stoke Common in Buckinghamshire. There is a doubtful record from Bagley Wood near Oxford.

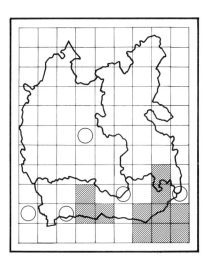
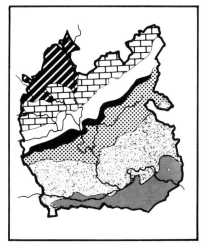

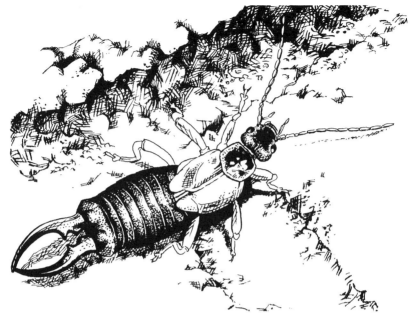

COMMON EARWIG
Forficula auricularia L.

The Common Earwig will be familiar to all readers: it occurs in every region of the British Isles including such remote places as St. Kilda, Shetland and the Isles of Scilly. Furthermore, in addition to its wide geographical distribution it favours a wide variety of habitats, including gardens and frequently wanders into houses. It would seem reasonable to suppose that if searched for, this insect might be found at any locality in the three counties.

Adults are variable in length (c. 15–20 mm) and are easily identified by their comparatively large size, dark brown colour, fully developed wings and by the shape of the male forceps (fig. 22a). The forceps are elongated in some individuals, whilst rare specimens have asymmetric forceps. Nymphs are smaller, wingless and grey-brown.

Common earwigs can be found in almost any situation. Efficient methods to determine their presence in a locality include the turning over of stones and the beating of overhanging branches. Sometimes, profuse numbers are seen, especially in coastal localities in late summer, where newly moulted adults can be found swarming under stones situated amongst dunes or on pebble beaches.

Adults can be found at any time of the year, but the general life cycle seems to begin with mating during the winter months, followed by the development of nymphs during spring and summer. Adult females lay their eggs in sheltered spots, such as in depressions in the soil under stones. The eggs are white and round. They show some maternal instincts in attending to the maturing eggs and nymphs.

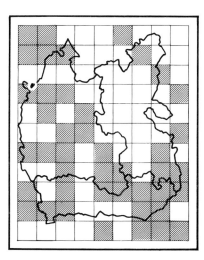
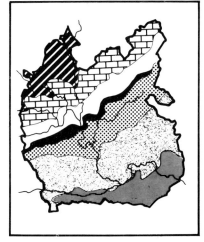

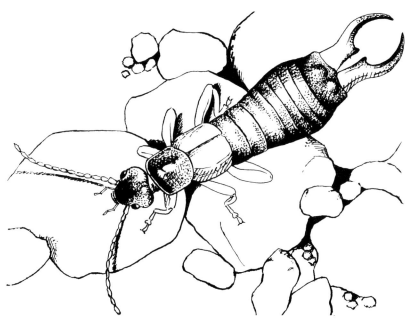

LESNE'S EARWIG
Forficula lesnei Finot

Compared with the Common Earwig, this is a smaller, more elegant species. The body and head are shiny, reddish brown; the legs, forceps and antennae being straw coloured. Unlike the Common Earwig, Lesne's Earwig does not have fully developed wings beneath its elytra. The forceps of the male are very distinctive in appearance, rendering confusion with our more common species impossible (fig. 22c). The forceps are covered with minute hairs. The general appearance of this insect is similar to that of a European species *F. pubescens* Gene with which it was confounded by earlier authors. Females resemble males but lack the distinctive forceps.

The author has found that the most reliable means of obtaining this species is to beat the branches of oaks which overhang areas of dry, coarse downland. Besides oaks, this species favours other deciduous trees and shrubs and also dense growths of wild clematis. Sometimes individuals may be seen basking on pieces of discarded cardboard on downland or climbing grass stems. Adults may be seen in good numbers throughout the months of August, September and October. Adults appear

89

to hibernate. Few adults are seen during the early part of the year.

This species, which is generally scarce and restricted to southern England as a British insect, has a nationally important focus of distribution in the upper Thames region. Comr. J.J. Walker took a male in a tuft of grass at Headington Wick (probably from a site now known as Sydling's Copse), near Oxford on 24 November 1906. When the author visited this locality in September 1986, the species was still there in numbers. Other historic records (in Lucas, 1920) include: near Wallingford, 1892; Bradfield College, near Reading; Streatley, 1905; Cothill, 1910; Kingston (?Bagpuise), 1840; Beckley, 1904. In 1986 this insect was present on three BBONT reserves: Dry Sandford Pit, near Cothill; Warren Bank, near Hailey; and Sydling's Copse. In 1986, the author beat three females from sloe by a field in Beckley and returned to the same site (Grid Reference: SP/565109) in September 1988 to beat four males (including a very dark specimen) from elms.

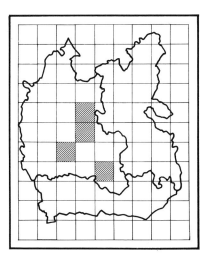
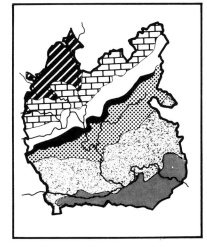

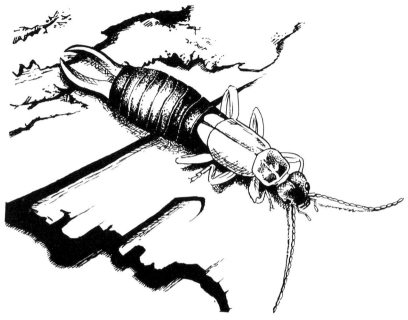

LESSER EARWIG
Labia minor (L.)

The Lesser Earwig cannot be confused with other British earwigs as it is distinctly smaller (total length about 8 mm) than other species. The early instars of our other earwigs may be of comparable size but they are clearly wingless and also paler than adults. The wings are well developed. The forceps are of comparatively simple structure and similar in males (fig. 22d) and females. The body colour is dark brown.

Lesser earwigs are seldom recorded in the region of the Upper Thames, but it is an insect which is easily overlooked. Its general appearance is like that of a small rove beetle or winged ant, so that this earwig is more likely to be noticed by the coleopterist or hymenopterist than by the orthopterist. Lesser earwigs are prone to fly and are reported to swarm over dung heaps in warm weather. The author has found this species by searching through rotting vegetation left behind on the bank after clearance of weed from a river.

In Britain this is an insect of wide distribution, being recorded from southern England northwards to Scotland and also in Ireland and is likely to turn up in any part of the three counties if searched for.

It is widespread in Europe and has been introduced to North America.

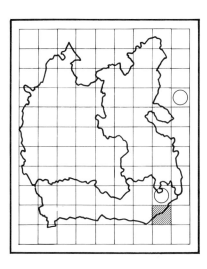

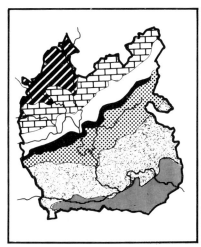

KEY TO NATIVE BRITISH ORTHOPTEROIDS

All species of orthopteroid insects native to the British Isles (with a few exceptions mentioned below) are included in the key. Introduced species of cockroach, the house cricket and migratory locusts are not included. Introduced cockroaches and the house cricket are seldom found far from heated buildings or rubbish dumps. The house cricket is very distinctive in appearance (see main text). Any cockroach may be compared with the illustration in the main text. If it does not seem to fit with any of these, it may be a nymph, or it may be one of the numerous species that are sporadically imported in foreign goods. In the Channel Islands there are two species of grasshopper not known from Britain. Jersey and Guernsey both have populations of *Oedipoda caerulescens armorica* Sellier; easily identified by its black-banded, blue hind wings. On Jersey one might find *Euchorthippus pulvinatus elegantulus* (Zeuner): it looks rather like *Chorthippus albomarginatus* (which has not been found on Jersey). The Lesser Mottled Grasshopper, *Stenobothrus stigmaticus* is known only from the Isle of Man as a British insect. Therefore it is not included in the key.

To make the key of greatest use to the general field naturalist, all the outdoor British orthopteroids are included (except for three species of stick-insect introduced to gardens in Devon and Cornwall on plants from New Zealand and the three grasshoppers mentioned above). An asterisk is placed next to those species recorded at some time from the three counties. The key refers only to adult examples: nymphs are often difficult to identify, especially those of groundhoppers and grasshoppers. One pair of British species is difficult to separate: the groundhoppers *Tetrix subulata* and *Tetrix ceperoi*. The latter species is unknown in the three counties and a full discussion of the points of recognition is beyond the scope of this book. Some help with the determination of these two species is given by the key and figures.

This key is designed to be simple and practical but the beginner may find its use a little daunting at first: for example, the wing bulge in grasshoppers of the genus *Chorthippus* may not seem to be very obvious. Unfortunately, such features are the only trusted means of identifying Orthoptera. The reader should remember that the habitat and song provide useful clues to the identity of species. There is no need to be discouraged; at the end of an introductory season's Orthoptera hunting the reader should be able to make reliable determinations of most species on sight.

1. Hind legs adapted for hopping . . . . Orthoptera: Saltatoria . . . 2.
– All legs similar . . . . Cursoria . . . 30.
2. Antennae short and comparatively stout . . . . Caelifera . . . 3.
– Antennae long and thread-like . . . . Ensifera . . . 16.
3. Pronotum greatly extended backwards over most or all of abdomen
(fig 12) . . . . Groundhoppers, Tettrigidae . . . 4.
– Pronotum not thus extended . . . . . Grasshoppers, Acrididae . . . 6.
4. Pronotum with prominent median keel (fig 13) . . . .
. . . . Common Groundhopper, *Tetrix undulata**
– Top of pronotum almost flat . . . . 5.
5. Larger; smoother; less mottled; may have short pronotum
(f. *bifasciata*); characteristic shape of head (fig 14a) . . . .
. . . . Slender Groundhopper, *Tetrix subulata**
– Smaller; rougher; more mottled; never with short pronotum;
characteristic shape of head (fig 14b); near south coasts of England
and Wales only . . . . Cepero's Groundhopper, *Tetrix ceperoi*.
6. Very large; glossy; tibia yellowish with black rings and black spines;
restricted to bogs and fens; (doubtful record from Berkshire) . . . . . .
. . . . Large Marsh Grasshopper, *Stethophyma grossum**
– Smaller species . . . . 7.
7. Antennae with distinct club-shaped endings . . . . 8.
– Antennae not obviously club-shaped . . . . 9.
8. Antennae with prominent white tips (fig 3a) . . . .
. . . . Rufous Grasshopper, *Gomphocerippus rufus**
– Antennae uniformly dark (fig 3b); small specimens; x-shape on
pronotum (fig 6f) . . . .
. . . . Mottled Grasshopper, *Myrmeleotettix maculatus**
9. Wings much reduced in length, exposing much of the abdomen in
females (fig 2a) and the tip of the abdomen in males (fig 2b); brown
knees, sides of pronotum gently incurved (fig 6b) . . . .
. . . . Meadow Grasshopper, *Chorthippus parallelus**
– Wings extending beyond tip of abdomen . . . . 10.
10. Slight bulge at base of wing (fig 9a) . . . . *Chorthippus* sp . . . 11.
– No such bulge . . . . 14.
11. Sides of pronotum nearly parallel (fig 6a) . . . . 12.
– Sides of pronotum incurved (fig 6c) . . . . 13.
12. Sides of pronotum almost parallel (fig 6a); knees not often
conspicuously dark; often with pale margin along fore-wing . . . .
. . . . Lesser Marsh Grasshopper, *Chorthippus albomarginatus**
– Sides of pronotum incurved (Fig 6b); dark knees; colour very
variable; wings of variable size but may be very large . . . .
. . . . long-winged
form of Meadow Grasshopper, *Chorthippus parallelus* t.explicatus**
13. Downy underside of thorax; black wedges on pronotum not reaching
hind margin (fig 8); tympanum as in fig 5a . . . .
. . . . Common Field Grasshopper, *Chorthippus brunneus**
– Smooth thorax; black wedges reach hind margin of pronotum
(fig 7) tympanum as in fig 5b; restricted to heaths near south coast of
England . . . . Heath Grasshopper, *Chorthippus vagans**
14. Female with ovipositor as in fig 11a; male with red hind tibiae;
distinctive venation featuring large median area (fig 9b); white
markings on wings (fig 10) . . . .
. . . . Stripe-winged Grasshopper, *Stenobothrus lineatus**
– Ovipositor as in fig 11b; median area much smaller . . . .
. . . . *Omocestus* sp. . . 15.
15. Underside of body beautifully coloured with glossy green and red
areas; conspicuous white palps . . . .
. . . . Woodland Grasshopper, *Omocestus rufipes**
– Underside of body yellowish or reddish; palps grey or pale brown
. . . . Common Green Grasshopper, *Omocestus viridulus**
16. Fore-limbs spade-like . . . . Mole Cricket, *Gryllotalpa gryllotalpa**
– Fore-limbs not spade-like . . . . 17.
17. Large, black and glossy; restricted to a few fields in Sussex . . . .
. . . . Field Cricket, *Gryllus campestris*.
– Appearance otherwise . . . . 18.
18. Wingless and coated in minute scales; restricted to Chesil Beach,
Dorset . . . . Scaly Cricket, *Pseudomogoplistes squamiger*.
– Appearance otherwise . . . . 19.
19. Small, brown with short wings; living on the ground amongst leaf
litter; records in Devon, Dorset, Wiltshire, Hampshire, Surrey and the
Isle of Wight, but generally scarce outside the New Forest . . . .
. . . . Wood Cricket, *Nemobius sylvestris*.
– Appearance otherwise . . . . 20.

20. Very large (c. 4 cm) and bulky; predominantly green in colour
. . . . 21.
– Smaller . . . . 22.
21. Bright green without obvious black spots; wings extending well
beyond tip of abdomen . . . .
. . . . Great Green Bush-cricket, *Tettigonia viridissima**
– Green (very rarely brown) with obvious black spots; recent records
being from a few sites in Dorset, Wiltshire, Sussex and Kent . . . .
. . . . Wartbiter, *Decticus verrucivorus*.
22. Cone-shaped head; slender body; green (rarely brown) with dorsal
stripe . . . . *Conocephalus* sp . . 23.
– Head not cone-shaped . . . . 24.
23. Ovipositor distinctly curved (fig 17i), wings not reaching tip of
abdomen (except in very rare f. *burri*, males of which form may be
difficult to distinguish from the following species) . . . .
. . . . Short-winged Conehead, *Conocephalus dorsalis**
– Ovipositor straight (fig 17h); wings long; at present restricted to
coastal regions of southern England, but species is gradually
spreading inland . . Long-winged Conehead, *Conocephalus discolor*.
24. Green all over when viewed from a distance . . . . 25.
– At least partly brown . . . . 26.
25. Covered in minute brown spots; females wingless; male with short
wings . . . . Speckled Bush-cricket, *Leptophyes punctatissima**
– No such spots; wings well-developed . . . .
. . . . Oak Bush-cricket, *Meconema thalassinum**
26. Brown and wingless; curved ovipositor (fig 17d) . . . .
. . . . female Dark Bush-cricket, *Pholidoptera griseoaptera**
– Obvious wings, if only short flaps . . . . 27.
27. Dark brown; yellowish wing remnants a few mm long . . . .
. . . . male Dark Bush-cricket, *P. griseoaptera**
– Wings more than a few mm long . . . . 28.
28. Grey or brown (but newly moulted individuals may be partly green)
with dark speckles; seldom found far from the coast . . . .
. . . . Grey Bush-cricket, *Platycleis albopunctata*.
– White margin to pronotum; brown or green . . . . 29.
29. Pronotum with white margin as in fig 16b; ovipositor as in fig 17f,
bogs and heaths . . . . Bog Bush-cricket, *Metrioptera brachyptera**
– White margin to pronotum as in fig 16a; ovipositor as in fig 17g . . . .
. . . . Roesel's Bush cricket, *Metrioptera roeselii**
30. Slender; pincer-like appendages . . . . . earwigs, Dermaptera . . . 31.
– Flat bodies; head concealed by pronotum . . . .
. . . . cockroaches, Dictyoptera . . . 35.
31. Very large; male markings; quite unlike the Common Earwig; sea cliffs
and beaches; possibly extinct in Britain . . . .
. . . . Tawny or Great Shore Earwig, *Labidura riparia*.
– Smaller . . . . 32.
32. Very small (a few mm) but with fully developed wings . . . .
. . . . Lesser Earwig, *Labia minor**
– Larger . . . . 33.
33. Fully developed wings; elytra with pale markings; male forceps as in
fig 22a . . . . Common Earwig, *Forficula auricularia**
– Wingless; usually small species . . . . 34.
34. Body reddish; limbs and forceps pale; male forceps as in fig 22c . . . . .
. . . . Lesne's Earwig, *Forficula lesnei**
– Male forceps as in fig 22e; unknown beyond Kent, Essex and East
Anglia . . . . Short-winged Earwig, *Apterygida media*.
35. Glandular hollow on seventh abdominal segment (fig 20) . . . .
males . . . . 36.
– Seventh segment without special organs . . . . females . . . 38.
36. Without tubercle in glandular hollow (fig 20b), body pale brown with
speckles . . . . *Ectobius pallidus**
– With tubercle in glandular hollow . . . . 37.
37. Tubercle as in fig 20c, smaller species, slender, grey in colour . . . . . .
. . . . *Ectobius panzeri*
– Tubercle as in fig 20a, larger species, slender, grey in colour . . . .
. . . . *Ectobius lapponicus**
38. Wingless, small species . . . . *Ectobius panzeri*
– With wings, larger species . . . . 39.
39. Large wings which cover abdomen, general appearance as in males of
the same species . . . . *Ectobius pallidus**
– Tip of abdomen exposed . . . . *Ectobius lapponicus**

DIAGRAMS OF SONGS

The following diagrams are reproduced from Ragge (1965) by kind permission of the author.

Diagrams of the songs of the British grasshoppers

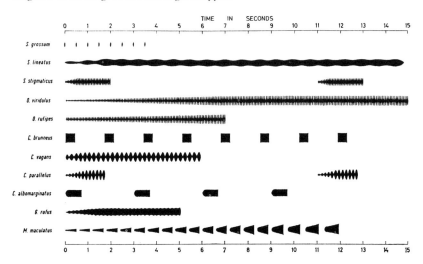

Diagrams of the songs of the British bush-crickets

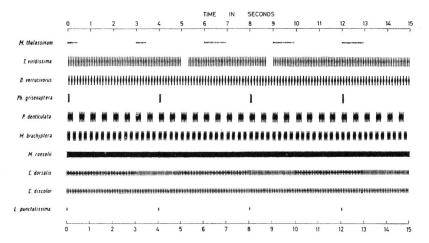

SELECTED BIBLIOGRAPHY

CORNWELL, P.B. (1968). The Cockroach. Volume 1. London.

HAES, E.C.M. and MARSHALL, J. (1988). Grasshoppers and allied insects of Britain and Ireland. Harley Books: Colchester.

LUCAS, W.J. (1920). British Orthoptera. London.

LUCAS, W.J. (1926). Orthoptera. In *The Natural History of Oxford*. Ed. Walker, J.J. Oxford University Press.

RAGGE, D.R. (1965). Grasshoppers, Crickets and Cockroaches of the British Isles. Warne: London.

ROTH, L.M. WILLIS, E.R. (1957). The medical and veterinary importance of cockroaches. *Smithsonian Misc. Coll. 134*:1–147.

MUSEUMS

Those wishing to conduct serious studies may wish to consult the material held by national and regional museums. They include: ·
British Museum (Natural History), Cromwell Road, London, SW7.
Hope Entomological Collections, at the University Natural History Museum, Oxford.
BERKS: Museum and Art Gallery, Blagrove Street, Reading, RG1 1QL.
BUCKS: County Museum, Church Street, Aylesbury, HP2 2QP.
OXON: County Museum, Fletchers House, Woodstock, OX7 1JH.

SOCIETIES

Berkshire, Buckinghamshire and Oxfordshire Naturalists Trust (BBONT). 3 Church Cowley Road, Rose Hill, Oxford OX4 3JR.
Amateur Entomological Society c/o 355 Hounslow Road, Hanworth, Feltham, Middlesex.
Royal Entomological Society, 41 Queen's Gate, London, SW7 5HU.

JOURNALS

Entomologist's Record and Journal of Variation c/o 31, Oakdene Road, Brockham, Betchworth, Surrey RH3 7JV.
Entomologist's Monthly Magazine, Brightwood, Brightwell, Wallingford, OX10 0QD.
Bulletin of the Amateur Entomological Society c/o 355 Hounslow Road, Hanworth, Feltham, Middlesex.
Entomologist's Gazette, E.W. Classey Ltd., P.O. Box 93, Faringdon, SN7 7DR.

RECORDING

A national atlas of British Orthoptera is being compiled. All records should be sent to P.T. Harding, Monks Wood, Abbots Ripton, Cambs. The National Scheme Organiser is Mr. E.C.M. Haes.